YOU ARE STRONGER THAN YOU THINK

HOW TO AWAKEN THE SUPERHERO WITHIN

JUSTIN LEVENSON

FOREWORD BY DR. YANJUN MA, M.D. PH.D.
AND DR. STEPHEN W. CLARK, M.D., PH.D.

YOU ARE STRONGER THAN YOU THINK: How to Awaken the Superhero Within is neither a diagnostic tool nor a medical text and is not intended to replace or modify therapy or the diagnostic and medical advice of a licensed practitioner. The advice and strategies contained herein may not be suitable for every situation. This work is sold with the understanding that the Author and Publisher are not engaged in rendering legal, medical or other professional services. Neither the Author, Editor nor the Publisher shall be liable for damages arising here from. The fact that an organization or website is referred to in this work as a citation or a potential source of further information does not mean that the Author or the Publisher endorses the information that the organization or website may provide or recommendations in it may make. Further, readers should be aware that Internet websites/applications listed in this work may have changed or disappeared between when this work was written and when it is read.

Published by Lev's House Entertainment

Copy Edited by: Norbert J. Sieber
Book Cover Design by Lauren Ledbetter
Book Design Layout by Luellyn Latocki Hensley

ISBN: 978-1-7337643-1-5

You are stronger
than you THINK!

Justin Yuma

DEDICATION

This book is dedicated to my loving and supportive parents Bonnie and Judd Levenson who were my first teachers in this life and the first people to begin teaching me about the amazing power of the human mind. Also, to my sister Noelle and my nephew Troy, whose love, patience and support have been instrumental throughout my life and especially during my cancer journey.

I love you all more than I can put in words.

CONTENTS:

A SPECIAL INVITATION
Powerful Healing Affirmations

When you or someone you love receives a cancer diagnosis, activating the healing power of your mind is a very important part of your healing process. This is why I want you to have these powerful affirmations that I used during my cancer journey. These will help you heal your mind and body, reduce anxiety and ... get better sleep.

Visit JustinLevenson.com/strongerthanyouthink for these special gifts.

Please connect with me personally on Facebook, Instagram and Twitter @JustinLevenson, or at JustinLevenson.com

I look forward to connecting soon.

A NOTE FROM JUSTIN

This book is all about my journey, about my reflections on it and my insights into empowering mindfulness that can spark lasting change in your body, mind, and spirit. This book has also been graced with the wisdom and experience of two brilliant, world-renowned oncologists who were with me throughout my cancer journey, Dr. Yanjun Ma, M.D. Ph.D. and Dr. Stephen W. Clark, M.D., Ph.D. I am extremely grateful for their support and willingness to contribute their perspective from a professional standpoint in the foreword that follows. My cancer journey is a beautiful combination of Western medical science under the care of these doctors and their teams, as well as my passion for the powerful connection between our minds and our bodies. The ability to activate this healing combination lives within everyone, empowering all of us to create an environment for emotional, physical and spiritual healing in our lives.

FORWARD
The Awakening

First impressions are often so important in life, and this holds true for patients with cancer. As an oncologist and neuro-oncologist, we often tell patients there is this "thing" we call the "door-way view" that we define by how the patient looks when we first see them. If we enter a patient's room, and the patient has family present, and we can't tell who the patient is or if we don't see anyone that looks sick, this usually indicates a good prognosis for the patient. This concept has been more refined for clinical trials and is called the patient's "Karnofsky Performance Status" or KPS (1). The KPS score is essentially, how well the patient can live their daily life, unassisted. A high KPS means the patient is very self-sufficient and portends a good prognosis, whereas, a low KPS means the patient requires assistance during their daily life and usually has a worse prognosis. This connection between KPS and prognosis was our first sense that patient prognosis is not solely determined by the pathology of their tumor or by their diagnosis but by "external factors", such as KPS, that can impact prognosis significantly.

Our memory of Justin's first visit with us still stands out. He was this vibrant, young man, full of energy, with an outlook that was simply captivating. This is not our typical impression of cancer patients during their first visit. Understandably, they often are very anxious, concerned, and simply terrified about having cancer. However, from the very beginning, Justin had this determination, this attitude, that he would conquer a disease that rarely loses a battle. His positive attitude continued with each subsequent visit and over time we became friends and we learned more about his personal philosophy toward the mindbody. Justin's philosophy about the mind-body is important for patients with brain tumors but is also important for cancer patients in general, especially in light of new findings that have led to us to rethink what we know about cancer biology and how the mind-body affects it.

The two most common questions we get asked by our cancer patients are: 1) Is there anything else they can do in addition to taking the chemotherapy? And 2) Can we recommend a special diet to help fight the cancer? These are excellent questions and we often feel our answers are too vague and too unsatisfactory. Our response to the latter question is that they should eat a diet full of fruits and vegetables or just a "healthy diet". Our answer to the former question is that they should try to remove all daily stressors, at least those in which they have some control over, and to reduce stress they don't have control over by using exercise and mediation. We tell them that stress is the one thing they have to manage, that your doctor can't, and that they should go to war on stress. We will explain later why stress reduction and a positive outlook is so important when fighting cancer.

Historically, medical training focuses on the disease and its treatment, without any emphasis on the mind-body. The reason for avoiding the mind-body was simple; there was no medical knowledge about it and no real sense that it even existed. The reason for this is indeed because the "brain" was and is the last frontier of medicine, and even today we still don't fully understand many functions of the brain. For example, "consciousness" or how we as humans know that we exist or that we are here is not well understood (2). Thus, the understanding of how the brain and body interact, other than through neuro-anatomy, was simplistic at best. Moreover, the thinking in medicine tends to be linear, for example, in cancer we learned that cancer was made of cells from the body, and to treat cancer, the idea was to attack the cancer cells with chemotherapy and destroy the tumor. The initial studies with mustard gas were initially successful for certain lymphomas and the search for a magic bullet for all cancer intensified (3). Initially, the thinking was what worked for one cancer would work for another, so patients with different tumors were given similar chemotherapy. However, we learned that not all cancers responded to the same chemotherapy. This led to an understanding that different cancer types harbor different genetic mutations, thus lung cancer and breast cancer respond differently to the same chemotherapy because they have different DNA mutations. However, the rabbit hole of cancer goes deeper, as even patients with the same cancer (i.e. same pathology such as breast cancer) can have very different responses to the same chemotherapy. We then learned that each patient's tumor, even if it is the same type of tumor (i.e. breast cancer) can have different mutations, for instance not all breast cancers are the same genetically (i.e. different breast cancers can have different DNA mutations). This difference between patients with the same type of cancer is called "interpatient heterogeneity" (4). Thus, in clinical trials, some patients respond to the study drug, whereas others don't respond, and we now think that this is mostly due to interpatient heterogeneity. But the complexity continues, and we soon learned that different parts of the same tumor from the same patient could be different genetically; this difference within a person's tumor is called "intrapatient heterogeneity" (4). All this complex heterogeneity meant that the idea of a single monolithic chemotherapy (i.e. magic bullet) for cancer patients was naive and would likely fail. From this realization came the idea of "targeted therapy" or "precision medicine" the idea of a tailored therapy targeting the patient's own mutational background (i.e. the patient's tumor DNA mutations).

The long journey of knowledge from monolithic chemotherapy to targeted therapy began in earnest on December 23, 1971, when President Nixon declared "War on Cancer" with the National Cancer Act. Since this time hundreds of billions of dollars have been spent around the world to combat cancer, with the National Cancer Institute's 2018 budget being 5.96 billion (5). The progress on treatment in cancer has been painfully slow mostly due to our lack of knowledge; and even though, little progress on treatment was made, our knowledge about cancer has expanded. Most of this money was spent on understanding the heterogeneity pro lem as mentioned above, but recently two promising findings have emerged. The first is that tumors are not static cells, that is, they evolve with time and by evolving they pick up new mutations that the initial tumor did not have. The second is that the body's defensive mechanism is an untapped therapy that could help with the heterogeneity problem.

These new research findings have led to an awakening in cancer biology. While the field of oncology transitioned to the idea of precision therapy, one question remained unresolved. Why does the body's immune system not recognize a tumor as being different from the normal body? Recently, new research found the answer. It seems tumors develop an uncanny ability to cloak themselves from the body's immune system (6). Thus, as tumors grow, they do so without any notice by the immune system. This is unfortunate, as the immune system is designed to seek out "infections" usually from bacteria or viruses and attack the cells that are infected. The power of the immune system comes from its ability to change and adapt to changes in bacteria or to different types of bacteria or infections. If this adaptive power could be harnessed, it might become a way to fight tumor heterogeneity and tumor evolution. Further research has shown that just as molecules called immune checkpoint inhibitors have been found that can block the cloaking mechanism, in some cancers they can be very affective therapies (6). For instance, in metastatic melanoma, a disease with very poor prognosis, if patients are treated with immune checkpoint inhibitors, around 30% of the patients will have a complete response, that is, the tumor is eliminated from the body in these patients (7). Thus began a new era called immune therapy with the use of immune checkpoint inhibitors and with clinical trials using these molecules in the treatment for most human cancers.

Immune therapy has reignited excitement about using the immune system to attack cancers and current research on brain tumors and other cancers is trying to find out how we can supplement immune checkpoint inhibitors, so they work in all patients and not just in the 30% responders. This has also led to more thoughts on another perplexing issue in cancer treatment, that is the "placebo effect". The "placebo effect" is something that is observed in almost every clinical trial and it's where some patients have a dramatic response to treatment even though they have been assigned to the placebo arm, that is, the pill they took was not the study drug but was a pill of an inert substance. How is this possible? In the placebo arm, there is nothing special, except for the standard of care, so why do some patients respond to the placebo therapy? It's important to note, that in clinical trials that have a placebo arm or therapy, neither the doctor nor the patient know if the patient is getting the actual study drug or if the patient is getting the placebo. This results in some patients that are taking the placebo thinking they are taking the actual study drug. The current thinking is that the placebo effect occurs because the idea of taking the study drug in essence stimulates the patient's immune system by activating dopaminergic neurons in a part of the brain's reward system called the ventral tegmental area (VTA). VTA activation then increases the immune system response and leads to these patients doing better even though they are only taking the placebo (8). Thus, this implies that the immune system can respond to the positive emotions patients have when taking medications, even if the medications are not active. This leads to the idea of the mind-body and the placebo effect is a good example of how a good "mind-body" can lead to a better result for the patient. Thus, any therapy, ideas or philosophy that can increase the positive aspect of the mind-body should have a positive impact on the patient's treatment. This, likely, will be the future of oncology, a combination of medical therapies that uncloak the tumor and allow the immune system to find the tumor and destroy it and other therapies that are used that strengthen the immune system, so that it works as efficiently as possible.

This is why Justin's philosophy is so important to understand and to practice. In his book he has taken his daily routine including both his physical and mental routine and given us a glimpse at what it takes to make the mind-body as strong as it can be. We believe that by using his methods of positive affirmation, this will generate a positive mindset, and in turn, will directly impact the immune system and lead to patients living longer and happier lives. Moreover, it is our hope that his philosophy will be the beginning of a new era of cancer therapy, one that includes both immune/chemotherapy in conjunction with mindbody training.

Dr. Yanjun Ma, M.D. Ph.D. and Dr. Stephen W. Clark, M.D., Ph.D.

BIBLIOGRAPHY

1. Yates JW, Chalmer B, McKegney FP. Evaluation of patients with advanced cancer using the Karnofsky performance status. *Cancer* 1980, 45(8): 2220-2224.

2. Dehaene S. Consciousness and the brain. (2014) New York.

3. Mukherjee S. The emperor of all maladies. A biography of cancer. (2010) New York.

4. Bedard PL et al. Tumour heterogeneity in the clinic. *Nature* 2013, 501(7467):355-364.

5. https://deainfo.nci.nih.gov/grantspolicies/finalfundltr.htm

6. Ascierto PA and McArthur GA. Checkpoint inhibitors in melanoma and early phase development in solid tumors: what's the future? *J Transl Med.* 2017,15:173.

7. Callahan MK. Immune checkpoint therapy in melanoma. *The Cancer Journal* 2016, 33(2):73-80.

8. Ben-Shaanan TL et al. Activation of the reward systems boots innate and adaptive immunity. *Nature Medicine* 2016, 22:940-944.

INTRODUCTION

"This is going to be the most amazing positive experience of my life. I am going to help so many people through this experience. This does not happen to someone like me, in this way, for no reason."

Three simple phrases, 37 words and a whole lot of positivity...these were the first words out of my mouth the moment I found out that I had a brain tumor!

It was February 3rd, 2014...a typical post-Super bowl party type of Monday. I was working through a nice hangover from the night before, working through my daily lists at my job at SESAC and thinking about what I was going to cook for dinner that night for my two good friends DP and Jacoby. This was a normal day in the life...or so I thought. My last memory that day was seeing the clock on my Windows desktop read 12:30 pm and then BOOM. The next thing I remember took place forty minutes later and was me, waking up on my office floor, surrounded by paramedics, being asked who the President of the United States was. After being escorted out of SESAC on a stretcher, and a short ride in one of Nashville's finest ambulances, I found myself sitting in the ER at Vanderbilt University Medical Center-one of the best hospitals in the world! At this time, we weren't really sure what had happened to me, although, based on what some of my colleagues had witnessed, I had fallen out of my chair and possibly had a seizure. I quickly was taken for a CT scan and when that came back "irregular," I was introduced to the wonderful world of an MRI machine and lovingly escorted back to my room.

There I was, sitting alone in my ER room, my parents waiting for me to call on the other end of a cell phone, to find out if they need to come up from Birmingham, AL, when there is a knock at the door. Knock, Knock, Knock...." come in" I cautiously answered, and five doctors slowly walked into my room. Their message for me was that I had a brain tumor in my left frontal lobe. My immediate response to this news was "This is going to be the most positive experience of my life. I am going to help so many people through this experience. This does not happen to someone like me, in this way, for no reason." It is fair to say that their jaws hit the ground...hell, I think I was older than all of these great people and I am pretty sure that they had never imagined hearing my response to their news. I quickly called my parents and told them "...it is time to come on up here..." and what followed that moment was the most intense two and a half weeks of my life.

The next day we met with one of Vanderbilt's top neuro surgeons, Dr. Kyle Weaver, and he told me that I had a seizure that was caused by an "egg-shaped" tumor and that we needed to remove the tumor in surgery, and that it was quickly scheduled for February 20th-a very short timeline in the medical world which I later learned was because of the severity of my tumor. Dr. Weaver told us that he thought it showed the signs of a good kind of tumor that was likely not cancerous. It is fair to say that this was at the very least, our interpretation of what Dr. Weaver told us because we were all still in a state of shock. A craniotomy...brain surgery...on my big noggin, was about to happen in just over two weeks. Whoa!

I remember having dinner with my parents after that initial appointment, talking about how excited we were that it was likely not cancer and my dad saying, "at least it's not brain cancer Justin." We were all trying to grasp what was taking place and trying our best to make plans for what we knew, and the huge world of information that we didn't know yet. It was a tense time in my world!

Despite the tension, the stress and the anxiety, I did what I knew best and what I had done from the very first moment I knew I had a brain tumor...I was thinking 'positivity' and working to manifest the outcome I so desired...to live! Positive thinking had been something I often talked about...hell, sometimes I would come close to preaching about it. I had grown to a place of total confidence in the power of my subconscious mind and quickly saw this brain surgery as an amazing way to practice what I had been preaching. And so, we did.... not just me...but the community around me.

My initial affirmations and vision centered around surviving brain surgery...because you know if that didn't happen, nothing else mattered! :) And so, I pulled out the mental paint brushes in my mind and started to paint the picture of surviving brain surgery. It started with me waking up in the recovery room flirting with the nurses. If you know me, you know I am a flirt...but this wasn't about flirting to meet an amazing woman or get lucky. Waking up flirting with nurses was what would happen when I survived brain surgery with my personality intact. The next part of my mental picture was waking up and having an erection because when that happened, it meant that I did not wakeup from surgery paralyzed from the waist down. This was really important because there was a significant risk of this based on where the tumor was and as a 35-year-old, single male, what do you think I thought of when they told me I could be paralyzed from the waist down? The final part of the picture I was painting was the doctor telling us that it was a perfect procedure. The idea of perfection works for me because I understand that word to mean complete, divine, the way things are supposed to be, etc. And so, the picture and mantras were coming together. My family, friends and I were focused on a "perfect procedure" and my close friends and family knew about this picture I had painted in my mind. A perfect procedure, that left me alive, fully functioning with my personality intact!

During the two and a half weeks between seizure and surgery, I grew a lot and tried to prepare in many ways. From planning post-op logistics, to a medical power of attorney and a will and even creating a list of every single account and password I could think of. I was preparing to die if it came to that, while focusing my energy and my mind on a beautiful life post-surgery.

The day of surgery came quickly and once checked in at Vanderbilt, I said my goodbyes to my dad and sister and my mom and I went upstairs. Before I left the hospital lobby, I handed my dad my cell phone and he had instructions to post an update to my Facebook page after surgery, to let everyone know how successful it was. My dad's post on my Facebook page, from February 20th, 2014 at around 12:05 PM CST:

"This is Justin's dad. He's out of surgery and joking with the nurses. Surgeon says it went superb, actually routine."

I survived and was thriving...and thanks to the amazing team at Vanderbilt, a supportive community, and my ability to leverage the powerful connection between my mind and my body, I am alive to tell you all about it!

CHAPTER 1
The Genesis of my 'Mind-Body' Transformation

Throughout this book, you will accompany me through the first fifteen months of my cancer diagnosis, brain surgery, and recovery and witness how I chose to live, think, and grow through this trying time. This collection of blog posts and current reflections have been curated to inspire you, and to share some of the impactful tools I have learned from others. I want you to know how these tools have impacted my life and helped me, with the hope that you may find a way to incorporate one or all of them into your life to create more peace in your life and spark positive change in your body, mind and spirit.

My hope is that this book, these words and reflections, help make your moment a little brighter and that they serve as an instrument of hope. A real-life story about how one soul faced life and death, during a tough time and how this growth has illuminated great possibility for all of us to heal, grow and love!

Long before I was a brain surgery and cancer patient, I was a student of the mind and a seeker of information about how to maximize the human potential and connect mind and body in a deep and meaningful way. This passion was ignited when my parents gave me a book on July 5th, 2000 titled *The Power of Your Subconscious Mind* by Dr. Joseph Murphy.

Wow...this book spoke to me and was the first book that I actually wanted to read. It just made sense to me. The primary circuitry that is important to emphasize is my strong belief in, and use of, my subconscious mind to create peace and abundance in my life, to heal emotionally, physically and spiritually, and to manifest my dreams. You may know this as "The Law of Attraction" and books/movies like *The Secret* brought these philosophies to the forefront of modern, Western culture. This "secret" is not a top-secret power that is only given to a select few, but instead, is the ability we all carry within ourselves, to be intentional with our thoughts, words and actions. Through what I often refer to as "conditioning yourself to have a positive mindset," we are able to "condition" ourselves to default to the positive and be aware when we don't. When I speak about "conditioning", I am simply talking about creating new habits in our lives to expand our consciousness and grow closer to our best self!

Before I go on, don't mistake this as any claim of perfection...it is not about perfection, but rather **consistent practice and trusting the process.**

In an effort to help share what I have learned and make it actionable, I have broken things down to the core of how I approach this area of my life. They are to: affirm positively, visualize and feel your dreams, and take consistent action while you trust the process...the exact tools that my family, friends and I used as I prepared for brain surgery and throughout my cancer treatment and beyond.

The idea of positive affirmations may not be new to you, but just in case it is, a positive affirmation is an action-based statement and often starts with phrases like "I am...", "I have...", "My life is...", etc. I use this form of positive self-talk in every area of my life, from the big goals of having financial freedom to smaller goals of a safe trip home with affirmations like "I have financial freedom" and "My trip will be uneventful".

During much of my cancer treatment, I used affirmations such as "I am healing perfectly" and "my body is responding perfectly to treatment" to help manage the anxiety I was feeling in that moment and continue to plant healthy seeds in my mind for the outcomes I so desired.

The first step is learning how to create affirmations that resonate with you and then to create and feel the pictures (visualizations) of you fully realizing those goals. We will talk more about them later but the three key points to remember are:

- Affirm Positively
- Visualize and Feel your Affirmations (dreams)
- Take consistent action and trust the process

Beyond these three core actions, there are several additional tools that I am learning about that continue to have huge impacts on my life and had a huge impact on my cancer journey. These include learning about our Subconscious Minds, Mantras, Meditation and Mindfulness, Self-Love and Living with Gratitude, Essential Oils, Nutrition, and Yoga. There is a wide variety of books on the market about all of these subjects and I write this as a fellow student with dreams of learning more, as I continue to walk my path to my best self.

As you will see in the following pages, which serve as a living example of my imperfect journey to my true and best self, **being patient with ourselves and trusting the process is very important.** We are all humans which means that we are all beautifully imperfect and this is great. I want you to know that despite our paths as a seeker, we are all likely to have tough days ahead, mishandle a situation or ten, get frustrated with our situation and with other people, and certainly be imperfect with how we learn and apply new things in our lives (like affirmations, yoga, nutrition, etc.). This is just how it is supposed to be. In perfect time on our own journey to our best self. Be kind to yourself.

I often reflect on the beautiful gift of self-awareness and how it is the first of two important steps to be mindful of when we show our human side (you know, those "imperfect" times). The first gift is for us to be self-aware that we have strayed from our best self, which I often refer to as our "center". Meaning, that we have reverted back to an unhealthy thought pattern, let our anxiety and fear take over our thinking, relapsed in an addiction, etc. Whether our center is tied to an organized religion, a non-religious spiritual path, or our own life-directing moral compass, the ability to lovingly be self-aware of when we have left this place is vitally important to our growth in this area.

The second gift is to lovingly bring ourselves back to our center by honoring our self-awareness and imperfection-being grateful, as we bring our focus back to where our best self knows it should be...to our center.

Over the course of the next seventeen chapters, I will be highlighting some of the tools I have been learning and using in my life, as they appear in the blog entries. I hope that through both the living example I have documented, and the combination of short summaries, videos, breathing exercises and powerful suggestions, you will be able to immediately find actionable inspiration and begin to make positive changes to your beautiful life today. I have also included a positive affirmation for each chapter that I hope you find useful. They were all used throughout my cancer journey and I continue to use many of these today.

So, for now, before you read further, take a very slow and deep breath through your nose, hold it for two seconds and exhale through your mouth with a verbal "AH...."

CHAPTER 2
BLOG #1 | 2.7.14
I Love you ALL!

Chapter Affirmation: **My surgery will be a perfect procedure.**

Well friends, the title says it all...well, almost!!

Let me start by telling all of you that I love you very much and appreciate how you have all enriched my life for the past 35+ years! Now let me catch you up on my week...it's been an interesting one for sure!

Monday started out the way most days start...some turkey bacon, a couple organic eggs, black coffee and weekly reports and emails at work. The last memory I have is at 12:06 PM CST when I read an email (and possibly sent one). The next memory I have is sitting in my office floor surrounded by paramedics. I was taken to Vanderbilt University Medical Center in a glamorous ambulance, where I was tested to determine what happened to me. After a CT scan came back "irregular", I had an MRI which showed a large tumor in the left frontal lobe of my brain! I seemed to have a seizure at work! This tumor has apparently been there for quite some time which may explain why my head is so damn big...haha...kidding! :) But seriously, I can rarely find a hat that fits, and I think I'd look pretty good in a hat! hahaha!

So....what now? First things first, the doctor believes that this has a 90% chance of NOT being cancer which is AMAZING!! Speaking of my doctor, he is a rock star who specializes in what I have...which btw, I forget the official name right now, but I'll share later! I have a surgery scheduled for 2/20/14 to remove all of the tumor...that's right folks...brain surgery! I am amazed at the peace I feel right now as I type those words..."brain surgery"...something that is arguably the most intense experience of my life thus far is in front of me and I am at a peace b/c I have ZERO control over anything but my attitude! I have always tried to live as positive of a life as I could and today I am thankful that there is no option but to be positive! The support and love from my family and friends has been the most amazing thing this week and I can't say thank you enough...well actually...I may get an opportunity to say thank you a lot b/c I can't drive a car for 6 months...fun stuff 'eh? :)

So... I started this blog (actually Romero started it for me...thanks Jon) and I am going to use this to keep everyone updated on things and hell, my family and close friends have pushed me to start writing for years so maybe this is what will finally get me going...I like the way it feels so far! I hope to go back to work next Monday and get back to "normal" as soon as I can! Speaking of work, I am so thankful to work for an amazing company like SESAC with the amazing family I work with. I am so lucky that this happened at work, where I am surrounded by people that love me and whom I love dearly! I have a day full of appointments on the 18th and then surgery on the 20th so in less than two weeks I will be recovering and 2 months from now I will be going in for the first post-op checkup, so things will move pretty quickly.

Please stay tuned to this blog and know that I love you, I am thankful for all of you and I look forward to many, many more amazing times, celebrating life together!

Love, Justin

Reflecting Back:
Wow, what a post to start out my blogging life! My first thought is that I am struck by the positivity that flowed from me during that time. I remember

being in those moments and smiling about the fact that, despite plenty of moments of uncertainty, fear, anxiety and worry, I was very positive at my core...at the center of my soul. It helped me prepare for what would become the biggest series of "practice what you preach" moments of my life. I especially connect with the thought at that time, that it was not cancer and a conversation my dad and I had after our first meeting with the surgeon, Dr. Weaver. We were having dinner and talking about how we were lucky that it was likely "not cancer" and I remember my dad saying "...at least it is not brain cancer!" HA...little did I know then that the deeply feared "C Word" would become part of my story and part of tremendous growth....growth that has led me to type these words on the page today! I find it to be very interesting that the thing I (and my family) feared the most, and even talked about at this dinner, would end up being part of my life's story. Perhaps it was the consistent focus on cancer that brought it closer to my experience? Or maybe a deeper reason like an intense experience for me to really grow through, you know in the way that only really uncomfortable experiences can do. I am not sure but I do know that the feeling of gratitude that my dad and I talked about that night, about it likely not being cancer, is very similar to the gratitude I wake up with every morning. Whether I have 1 more morning or 60 more years' worth of mornings left, my goal is to wake up every day and feel grateful. Grateful to be alive, grateful for my life, for all of my life's experiences and that is the best kick start to a day I can ever have! I am grateful!

Every day that you wake up is a gift, and every challenge that you face is an opportunity to grow closer to your best self. Having a positive attitude and living with gratitude are powerful ways to be intentional with your life and a great place to start. When these are part of your habitual thought pattern, you will notice that everything seems a little brighter and a little more in sync. This will be a huge shift in your life! When you are able to view life experiences through a positive lens (if even momentarily), you will be able to find opportunities to grow and heal through everything that comes your way.

The next time you experience something in your life that feels sad, scary or maybe it's just one of those days you wish you could press the reset button, see if you can hold at least one positive or grateful thought in your mind. Next, try asking yourself "how can I grow through this?". Every time that you insert this perspective into your life experience, you are changing how your mind is conditioned to experience life and are opening the doors even wider, to deep, powerful healing in your life.

CHAPTER 3
BLOG #2 | 2.10.14
Letting Go...and Letting Love In!

Chapter Affirmation: **I am open to love and to be loved. I am grateful for today and for everyone who loves me.**

Ok so I was not prepared for this love...hell, I don't even know if I ever contemplated this much love existing for me...and all I know to say is thank you, I love you too and I am opening myself up to receive as much of this love and support as I can! :)

From the time I posted my first blog entry Friday, my phone has not stopped ringing, dinging and beeping and every sound is the sound of you, my amazing family and friends, telling me that you love me and are thinking and praying good thoughts for me! I have been meaning to write again but just haven't been able to wrap words around how great you have made me feel! It has been completely mind-blowing to hear from so many of you and I hope you all know how much I absolutely appreciate you!

My weekend was pretty great! It was full of amazing people, relaxing self-reflection and some tasty food...seriously; Silo was amazing Saturday night and brunch at Pinewood Social was awesome!

I went back to work today, and it was so great to see my work family! I was surprised with super hero balloons, a beautiful card and a cake with my Superman picture on it...awesome!! The outpouring of love that is continuing to flow to me is overwhelming in the most amazing way and I just can't say 'thank you' enough!

I am feeling pretty great with the exception of my sore tongue and the anti-seizure medication they have me on, which just makes me feel a little out of it sometimes but hey, if I need it, I need it! I think this "letting go" is one of the most amazing things about this experience thus far and is really helping to keep a sense of peace in my life! I know I am in excellent hands at Vanderbilt, I have an amazing family and huge circles of friends and I know that I will come through this experience healthier, happier and more at peace than I have ever been before! I am focusing on letting go, staying absolutely positive and letting the love of my family and friends lift me up! It is amazing!

Thank you all for the continued positive vibes, prayers and whatever other positive energies you can send my way!

Justin

Reflecting Back:
"Letting go...and letting love in" is such a perfect place for me to have been at this point in the journey and in many ways, is where I continue to focus now...on letting go of what does not serve me and being open to what is ahead on my journey. Taking this a step further, it's about loving my true self more, so that I can love others more and share my love with the world. This idea of being thankful and loving is a big part of my life and certainly has been a big part of the past seven years. For most of my 20's and early 30's, I held real love away and thought that was because it was more fun to have freedom, be single, and do what I want to do when I want to do it. It was all superficial and rooted in my desires...or at least what I thought I desired.

At this stage in my cancer journey, I realized that what I was really doing was not loving myself, which in turn, means that I was attracting amazing women that were not an amazing match for me. This makes perfect sense. Would a loving, open, vulnerable person really want to be with someone who spent more time judging than loving themselves? And would that even be a healthy relationship if I met that person? My answer to both of those is a loud NO. It was not until I started to judge myself less, and love myself more that my heart shifted. Actually, my entire world shifted. The more I became aware of my judgmental thoughts, the more I was aware of how to counter those with loving thoughts. You know, like when we stand in front of a mirror and our eyes immediately go the one spot on our body we feel is not attractive? Or how about when we look at a photo of ourselves and we immediately go to our face...do we have a double chin? Do we look ok? What about the area I hate about myself? Can you relate?

I know I can, and these are the types of things I was initially observing. It was only after I realized that my deepest insecurities were tied to the subconscious judgments I made about myself and others all day long, that I was able to really work on judging less, and loving more. Judging myself less and loving myself more. So now, when I stand in front of my mirror, I try to look at those areas of my body and think things like "you are looking good today" and work to keep my mind focused on being thankful and grateful...knowing I am doing the best I can!

During the early, pre-surgery stages of this journey, I was thankful for the love and support of friends, as well as the medical team at Vanderbilt. That team had been and would continue to work their compassionate magic to help me live a long and healthy life. I had the ultimate faith and trust in them and still do today. Between the inner peace I had from the start and the amazing reputation Vanderbilt has, I was able to peel back a few layers of anxiety (most of the time) and work to focus my mind on what I could control...the power of my positive mind. I say "most of the time" because I am human and am far from perfect. Going through intense experiences in our life can be hard, really hard...and I believe it is very important to own that beautiful imperfection and own our bad days! Hopefully even in the midst of our toughest days, we can find a thankful, grateful moment. That's the goal! Thankful...Grateful... Loving...these are still daily goals today...Thankfully! :)

Are you grateful? Scientists all over the world have studied the effects of gratitude for years and all agree that experiencing feelings of gratitude makes us more emotionally balanced, happier, and more positive. In fact, according to many recent studies, having truly grateful thoughts drastically decreases stress. I am not talking about just waking up and saying you are grateful (however, this can be a great place to start), but instead deeply recognizing something that you are grateful for and feeling that gratitude as much as you can. Similar studies also point to the fact that disease thrives in stressful environments which only serves to amplify the benefits of creating a habit around feeling grateful every day. An easy way to form new habits is to start small and my suggestion is that you have at least one grateful moment every morning for three weeks. Something simple like "I am grateful that I woke up today", "I am grateful that I am loved", "I am grateful that the sun is shining" or you can always go with something more personal that you can feel deeply. **The trick is to say it, think it and feel it deeply!**

CHAPTER 4
BLOG #3 | 2.13.14
When things got real...meditation stepped in to help.

Chapter Affirmation: **With every breath, I release what no longer serves me.**

Well you probably all knew it was going to happen...be honest...exactly... and you were right!

One of the fascinating things I am observing in myself through the first 10 days of this experience is the change of emotions that I am feeling! I was VERY comfortable with the logical part of this exercise like the percentages, the steps and process etc. I am even more comfortable and confident in the part of this story that helps me turn this into the most amazingly positive story in the world, in service to other people! But...this is the first time in my life that I have felt what seemed like uncontrollable anxiety...as in just not being able to "bottle it up", "manage it", "feel it and move on", etc. etc. etc. For the first time I am able to relate to people in my life that have felt anxiety that seems beyond their (our) own control in a whole new way!

But this isn't a sad story...AT ALL...first of all b/c I am alive to feel this (which is amazing) and b/c I am learning how to breathe through it!! I have practiced yoga on and off through the years but 5 short minutes of breathing...and bringing my mind back to breathing have really helped my day!

In full disclosure, I emailed my doctor's nurse to ask if they would write a prescription for an anti-anxiety drug and my mom and sister will testify about what a shock and change of course that is for me! But guess what...I can't have any for good medical reasons...you know...back to the whole letting go, trusting Vanderbilt thing!

This is where it got good for me today...I was directed to this great site by a friend of mine that contains free guided meditations and did a short, 5-minute breathing meditation! Wow!! What a difference a few purposeful breaths can make! I am really looking forward to diving into this website and more meditations in the coming days as I continue to prepare my body for a healthy, successful surgery! Hell, this will just help me sleep better too...plus my stomach called and would like me to untie the knots! :)

Thanks for all of the continued prayers, positive vibes, emails, texts, calls, FB messages, etc.! You have all continued to blow me away and I am forever thankful for you!

Cheers (with water)!

Justin :)

Reflecting Back:
Ah meditation...what a joy and gift it is to my life and to all of our lives when we welcome it in. The site I was referring to was hosted by UCLA and was my first real step into the world of meditation and wow...after the first 5 minutes I was hooked. The immediate release of tension and anxiety and increase in peace was felt through my entire being. It seriously helped me in every small moment. (You know, like the ones that feel like massive moments or really bad days.) It also certainly helped in the bigger picture of managing stress and anxiety and creating an environment for total healing in my body. I am thankful for this today and love that I was openly thankful for this in 2014. I will never claim

to be perfect at this and still strive to be in a consistent practice of daily meditation...let's face it...we are human and none of us are perfect...but the more I sit to meditate, the further I step into making this a daily habit. The more I sit to meditate, the more peace I feel, the more clarity I experience and the more I feel connected to my higher source and guides. Simply put, meditation gives our mind the time and space to unwind and for that, I am thankful!

For those of you who don't have a lot of experience with meditation, don't worry because you can do it very easily! Seriously, there is no "wrong way" to meditate and no reason to fear meditation. It is simply a process of you, finding a quiet, still place and taking a few minutes to focus your mind on the natural flow of your breath. You can start with 1 minute every day and work up to 10 minutes. I love meditating in the morning because it is a great start to my day but if that doesn't resonate with you, that's ok, the benefits are there for you any time. There are several great smart phone apps available today that do an excellent job walking Western audiences into the world of meditation. Two of my favorites are Headspace and Calm and both are available for you right now on your phone. Be kind to yourself as you start to form new habits and trust the process. Remember, it is all about giving your mind the time and space it needs to unwind and there is no "wrong way" to meditate. Enjoy!

CHAPTER 5
BLOG #4 | 2.17.14
It's Not You...It's Me! :)

Chapter Affirmation: **I move in the direction of what is best for me. My self-love is abundant.**

No really...I'm being serious! For the first time in my life, that phrase 'it's not you...it's me' makes sense!

As you know, my week was pretty intense...amazingly intense actually! My week was full of emotions at a new depth for me and as I sit here watching the sun set over Nashville, I feel pretty damn good about it! The one thing I don't feel great about is that I am missing a gathering at Tavern in my honor where that building is full of so many amazing people that came together to tell me how much they love me! Please know that I LOVE YOU TOO and that I wished I could make it! After the week I had and the week ahead of me now, I really felt that the best thing for me to do was to focus on relaxing, being low key and breathing! :)

HOWEVER...I see a couple of opportunities for awesome here that I want to quickly explore with you...

1. This means that you all MUST come to a post-recovery celebration of life (and that we will likely be able to use the excuse "to celebrate life" from here forward...sounds FUN!)

2. Tavern is full of amazing people from very different corners of

Nashville and I bet there is something started tonight...a romance, a business, a charity...hell...maybe a little bit of all three!

3. The GM may or may not have promised free unsweetened tea for life (for me) in exchange for all of the liquor and beer sales from tonight so please drink up...and cheers one or two for me! :)

Seriously friends, thank you very much! The past two weeks have been an intense opportunity to see rapid change in myself, take a look at death, feel more love than ever before and much more that I am forever thankful for! On the medical front, I had my first appointment with my oncologist today and that was great! This will be my main doctor moving forward after I fully recover from surgery! I was told that he thinks I have one of the rarest types of brain tumor and that it is also one of the "best" types of brain tumors to have (pathology will confirm)! It is interesting to be at peace knowing that I have the best kind of brain tumor I could have...WHOA...what a difference a couple week can make on your point of view! Life is good friends.... life is certainly good!

Thanks for the continued prayers and positive energy!

Justin

Reflecting Back:
As you may have guessed, my world was buzzing in the two weeks between my seizure and surgery. My days were full of a busy schedule with doctors, hangs with family and friends and a little time to myself to reflect and prepare for surgery...while also preparing the business of death, just in case things didn't work out the way everyone expected them to. Those two weeks were the most intense two weeks of my life at that point, and I can still agree with that statement today, almost seven years later. My close friends wanted to have a happy hour hang with our group of friends and a Nashville favorite, Tavern was the spot we

choose. What started out as a group of 10-15 quickly grew to an RSVP list of over 100. I remember being at Tavern having lunch with friends a couple of days before this event was scheduled and, on the way out, there was a line of friends that happened to be dining and working there and they all had amazing, loving words for me. As much as I appreciated all of that positive energy and support, I started to get a little nervous about showing up to a large event held in my honor for what I felt was like a funeral or visitation for me. I was experiencing a great deal of anxiety and nerves at this time. The two and a half weeks between the seizure and brain surgery were by far the most intense, anxious days of my life. The idea of having the same conversations about surgery, next steps, etc. all evening, while I was simultaneously working to manage my intense anxiety and nerves was a no-go for me and thus, I decided not to go and sent this post out as the event was starting. "It's not you, it's me" was the perfect way to say it and still rings true to me today. This was about self-care and self-love. I was aware of what I felt was best for me, I trusted my intuition and made the call to skip this one. I am thankful for the love and support of my community, and even more thankful that I listened to my inner voice and did what I felt was best for me.

Do you love yourself enough? No really, do you love yourself enough to listen to, and trust your inner voice when other influences disagree? Don't be afraid of loving yourself enough to change course, say no, or make a different decision. Self-love is an important step on the healing journey for all of us.

When you are facing adversity, being able to confidently listen to your inner voice, the wise teacher within all of us, will always lead you towards health, love and peace. This inner knowing is often referred to as your intuition or the voice of God and regardless of your spiritual beliefs and what you refer to it as, this knowing and wisdom is always there for you. Always.

The next time you are faced with any type of adversity, work to quiet your mind with a few slow, deep breathes, a short walk around your house or neighborhood or any other calming tool you love. The more you can quiet your mind, the louder your inner voice will speak to you.

CHAPTER 6
BLOG #5 | 3.3.14
So, You Really Meant "Rest"?

Chapter Affirmation: **My body is healing perfectly. I'm positively manifesting my dreams.**

Ok, Ok...so I thought I knew what "rest" meant...but I didn't...and my body let me know it!

A lot of amazing things have happened since my last blog, I've learned a lot and by far the most important lesson of the past 10 days is that when Vanderbilt doctors tell me to rest and do nothing for a minimum of two weeks, they really mean it. To be more specific, their definition of rest is much different than just resting my normal, music industry, *'go fast and hard'* lifestyle. It really means that I need to sit on my tail, binge on HBO Go, Netflix and Xfinity On Demand and do nothing. This "doing nothing" may be the hardest part about the post-surgery experience thus far! This is where I insert the voice of my neurosurgery nurse saying, "I told you so" (you were right Tracy)! When I chill, my body feels better...and some days, going to lunch in Cool Springs was enough to make me want to crawl back to bed!

The good news is that life is amazing and with every passing second, my body is healing, and I am feeling better! I have also been constantly reminded that I don't look like I had brain surgery and apparently have surprised my friends and family with how good I have looked...I think everyone (including me) thought I would look a lot worse than I do. With the exception of a "sexy", "awesome", "gnarly", "sweet" head wound (that is healing amazingly well), a sweet half-head shave, some forehead swelling and a slight black, left eye...you really can't tell that I had surgery! So, what this means is that when I wear the awesome hats my friends are making for me (thank you), nobody knows I just had a pretty damn intense surgery! Speaking of the actual surgery experience, I can't say enough amazing things about my team at Vanderbilt. It started with the ambulance staff, the ER staff, the oncology staff, the neurosurgery staff, the pathologists, operating room staff, ICU staff, nurses, etc. etc. etc.... everyone has blown me away with their extreme level of professionalism, attention to detail, bed-side manner, positive attitudes, kindness and just overall being amazing human beings! I feel lucky and blessed beyond belief and I am so EXCITED about the future.

The days leading up to surgery were intense my friends...VERY intense! I don't know that I have ever experienced more anxiety in my adult life and my surgeon, Dr. Weaver (a total bad ass btw) was absolutely correct when he told my parents and me that the two weeks between my first appointment with him and surgery would be the hardest part of this entire experience! I have always been an introspective person; someone who enjoys diving into my thoughts and emotions, analyzing them as I look for opportunities to grow and expand and these two weeks pushed me to new levels. At times, I questioned whether it was too much for me...so I dug deeper, cried a little, focused on some breathing, thought positive thoughts and things got better! Growth my friends...amazing, sometimes stressful...but always amazing growth! I've heard it said many ways but the thought that you will never be in a situation that you can't fully handle is appropriate here. I always strive to be positive, am passionate about encouraging others to be positive and still had a few moments of the most intense anxiety and stress that I have ever experienced that made being "positive" a challenge...BUT I MADE IT THROUGH....WOOOO HOOOOO! :) Further here, this means that you can too (we will get more into that on another day!)

The morning of surgery was tense for me and I can't even imagine what it was like for my family and friends...with one exception! I know that for some of my friends, it was chilly and pretty sleepless b/c they arranged to have the "Super J" t-shirts hung on the Music Row Roundabout statues and many were there cheering for me as we drove by at 5:00 AM! WOW!!! THANK YOU!!! Once I got to the hospital, my part was pretty easy...get in some surgery clothes, run some tests, say some "I Love You's" and then the anesthesiologist gave me "a couple martinis" and I was out like a light! Five hours later, I was flirting with the ICU nurses, realizing I still had movement in the lower half of my body (this was one of the risks of surgery based on where the tumor was) and on my way to what everyone at Vanderbilt tells me is one of the most amazing post-op recoveries they have ever seen! The first night in ICU was tons of fun...no really...TONS! I had to wake up every hour for neuro-checks, medicine, a 1:00 AM MRI and those beds...those SUPER comfortable beds! :) But, hell...I was alive, doing "amazingly well" and on track to be known as a "rock star" on the Neuro-ICU floor! Life was and is good...so very good! :) The next big milestone was the fact that about 24 hours after surgery, I was moved to the normal neuro floor which means I did so well, that I got to skip the "step down" floor and could have more visitors, could eat whatever I wanted to and could sleep in 4-hour blocks...the sleep was likely the biggest win for me b/c I was tired! OK...being able to see more friends and family was a huge win too...so awesome...but the sleep, the sweet sleep was needed! This also meant that my parents could go have a nice dinner, a couple cocktails, a full night's sleep and relax while knowing I was doing well after a "perfect" surgery!

By Saturday morning I was told I was being discharged and less than 48 hours after having brain surgery I was getting into my car and driving down 21st Avenue! That's right...less than 48 hours after surgery I was at my "home away from home" in Franklin, settling in with friends, taking a few more deep breaths and resting...or at least starting to learn what "resting" really means!! Thanks for the continued love, support, messages, calls and meals...I am humbled to have so many amazing people in my life and look forward to thanking you all in the months to come! Stay tuned b/c I promise to keep this blog active as I move into the next phases of this journey!

Much love!

Justin

Reflecting Back:
Well this one covers a lot of ground and I am almost at a loss for words right now. After reading this blog for the first time in years, I want to head right to Vanderbilt and hug everyone there! I am filled with such love, gratitude and joy that I want everyone there to be reminded that they are angels that do amazing work! I think it is important to point out an idea from this post that I often talk about. Perhaps this is more of a technique I use where I use words and time to manifest things in my life. When I say, *"The good news is that life is amazing and with every passing second, my body is healing, and I am feeling better!"* this is one tool I use to release anxiety and program my brain. It helps me to use time, in this case "...with every passing second..." to drive home the fact that what I am experiencing in this moment, and the next moment, is the creation or manifestation of my dream, of my desired dream and life experience. This is me trusting in the power of The Law of Attraction. I am trusting that by being consistent with the messages I send to my mind, I can create more positive experiences throughout my journey and over time, experience magnificent manifestations of my most sincere desires. The realization of my dreams. Said one more time... we can use our mind to help improve our experience immediately (like reduce our anxiety and stress) and spark lasting change in our lives, as we work to manifest our dreams.

Knowing that every second of my existence, my mind is working to create harmony and perfect health, helps me (and certainly did then) release some of the worry and fear that I was experiencing. This practice of speaking and thinking positively, helps me build confidence in my beliefs, as I continue to affirm what I want, and know it to be true. In this case, it is about my body healing perfectly. By affirming (thinking, speaking and feeling) that my body is healing perfectly, I was able to dial back the anxiety a few notches which in turn, allowed me to rest more completely. This also sent consistent messages that everything I was experiencing was my body responding perfectly and healing perfectly. I believed it to be true and so it was true. The more I affirmed this, the more it helped me. And during flareup moments of intense anxiety, sadness, fear or worry, just going back to the phrase "my body is healing perfectly" made a HUGE impact. I cannot stress this enough that this helped me in a big way, and it can help you too.

This daily practice of positive affirmations and visualizations has been a big part of my life for most of my adult life (thanks Mom and Dad). As recently as this morning, as I laid in bed, waiting on my girlfriend's alarm to ring, I was picturing my life growing, with every passing second, towards the realization of my dream to build a life and career helping, teaching and inspiring people to live a positive, balanced and more joyful life. I continue to affirm this and visualize it happening in my mind's eye and combine those images with deeply feeling the emotions that I associate with the realization of this dream.

Always remember that it is the combination of visualization and emotional connection to these visions that activates immense manifesting power in our lives! Think about a few goals you have for your life and then imagine how great you will feel when you accomplish these goals-I often refer to this as feeling the emotion of your win. Get as specific as you can and work to really hold onto how you are **feeling**. Once you identify the amazing emotions of your win, spend a moment, every time you think about it, deeply **feeling** how you will feel when you accomplish your goals. This technique will help **you and yours** in times of trauma and joy!

CHAPTER 7
BLOG #6 | 3.13.14
Healing Perfectly in the Suburbs!

Chapter Affirmation: **I will grow through this and become healthier and happier than ever before.**

Hello everyone...I hope life is amazing in your world!

It has been another great week of resting, recovering, healing and enjoying life in the burbs...the title of this blog post says it all! My doctors all tell me that I am continuing to heal very well and that they are blown away by the pace of my recovery and that my positive attitude remains as strong as ever-this is where I say, "I told you I was going to kick this in the ass and turn it into the most positive experience of my life"! :) My doctors have stressed that having a positive attitude and healthy diet are as helpful for my healing than anything they do at the hospital! The power of positivity is real, and I am living proof...I can't help but be positive and I believe that it is a direct result of how my parents raised me by planting and nurturing the seeds of positivity in me from a very young age! To take this thought a step further, my parents gave me a book called *The Power of Your Subconscious Mind* when I moved to Tennessee on July 5th, 2000. They told me that they had raised me with this book's principles and encouraged me to read it and let it enrich my life! Anyone that knows me well knows that this book has been a huge part of my life and I will talk more about this topic later, on the blog. I got my stitches removed last Wednesday which made my head feel better immediately and the actual incision is healing really well! I still have some swelling in my forehead which the doctors say is normal and will go away soon. This is great news b/c I think I look like a weird Halloween costume with a water balloon on my forehead...pretty weird to look at (ok and funny) but not a health concern at all. When I was discharged from the hospital, I was taking a TON of medicine, but I am happy to report that as of Sunday I was only taking my anti-seizure medicine and Tylenol for the pain which is a HUGE win and yesterday I only needed to take two doses of Tylenol-this is another sign of my improving health! I am focusing on "emerging from surgery healthier, happier and more empowered to do great things" and "my body is healing perfectly" so if you are looking for things to focus on for me, those are two great phrases to send out to the universe! Thank you in advance! :)

It has now been 5 weeks since this adventure began, and it has certainly been a fast-paced, whirlwind of a journey! Over the past 5 weeks, there have certainly been plenty of ups and downs, plenty of happy times, a solid dose of anxiety and nerves and some low points...but I am still so much more excited about the future than nervous and feel so lucky to be able to go through this experience. To say my life is forever changed is an understatement and I am just starting to understand this new life that I have been given and understand that I may never fully understand this gift (which is totally ok). What I do understand today is that I am lucky to be alive and am loving the way the world looks from where I am sitting. Speaking of lucky, I am also lucky to have all of you in my life...seriously, you are amazing! I have been overwhelmed by your continued love, support, prayers, positive vibes, meals, sweet baked goods (although, it is almost pool time, so I probably need to cut down on those hahaha). I look forward to thanking you all in person and if you ever need it, being able to support you through any challenges that life throws your way!

I hope to be able to return to my home soon which will be great... but also a little sad b/c I have really enjoyed staying with my friends in Franklin! These two amazing people welcomed me into their home and have been awesome friends and hosts! It has also been great to be somewhat "off the grid" which has helped me rest, recover and thus be feeling really great and better every day! With that said, I can't wait to see more of my friends, sleep in my own bed and be in my little zen'd out corner of the universe! My suggestion to all of you is to tell your friends and family you love them today. Tell them how much they mean to you. Forgive them for the silly things we get pissed about (I am guilty of this too. Trust me!) And, when you think of them (like right now), send them a quiet "I love you"! This is powerful stuff...powerful energy and emotions...trust me, it feels great! :)

As a little FYI, you may not have been notified about my last blog post so, if you haven't read that, scroll down and check it out! This happened b/c my trial subscription of this blog site Populr had expired and as a result, all of my followers were not notified. The good news is that the amazing people at Populr helped me out and going forward, you will all be notified when I post a new blog-this is also a reminder to subscribe to the blog, so you get notified! :) I also want to encourage you all to check out Populr for your own blogging and website needs b/c this team of people are great!

I hope you all have a great rest of the week!
Justin

Reflecting Back:
Someone recently told me that "...the magic happens when someone lives what they teach..." and that was the first thought that hit me like a ton of bricks when I read this today. Looking back on this post, I am proud of myself and am happy to report that I am even more excited about the future than I was almost seven years ago...and in many ways, my current moments are spent working intently towards sharing more of my passions with the world-which is what I was envisioning back then. My mantra about my body responding perfectly and "...emerging healthier, happier, and more empowered to do great things" is so incredibly powerful and it is awesome to see how this has continued to

evolve in my life. One immediate example is the fact that the smile that radiates from my face when I think about this mantra is larger than life and full of truth and joy. I always held the image of being a better, more loving and healthier version of myself firmly in my mind-and still do as I type these words.

These "judge-free" affirmations (a little name I coined) are so impactful and I believe they are a direct result of what I had learned through that point and certainly what I continue to learn today. By focusing on larger, success-oriented/positive outcomes (like being alive, healthy, happy, empowered to live a life in service to others, etc.) we are able to quiet corners of our minds that may be the root of more destructive thought patterns...aka fears, anxieties and tension. In my life, I have found that when I have complete trust in these larger affirmations versus focusing on what I refer to as more "tactical affirmations" or smaller affirmations (like a positive outcome of a meeting or a first date, an uneventful car ride or flight, etc.) I am able to release layers of stress and anxiety in the immediate moments and in the larger context, plant powerful seeds for areas I want my life's path to realize.

During this time, I was healing from a massive, post-surgery head wound and found that my mind would play sneaky tricks on me if I let it. I remember lying in bed watching TV, feeling pretty good and then I felt a unique sensation in my head. There are a TON of things that my mind would race towards as I tried to self-diagnose myself. Trust me, none of them were very positive. When I started really focusing on my mantra of "My body IS healing perfectly" I was able to peel back a few layers of anxiety. This is because I knew that if my body was healing perfectly (which it was), then whatever I was feeling was what it felt like for my body to heal perfectly. This "judge-free affirmation" reduced my anxiety, and allowed me to rest more completely, which allowed my body to heal quicker and more completely. This is something that we can all start doing today. It is all about trusting the process!

This post is also a great example of me working to own all of the moments and emotions ("ups and downs"), not just the positive ones. Let's face it, life is likely not going to be perfect and we will all have more opportunities where our positive mental attitude is tested and that is something to celebrate. I celebrate this because every one of these "less than positive" moments provides us an opportunity to come back to our positive mind, to come back to our center and that is powerful. In the same way meditation teachers (and smart phone apps) coach us to bring our attention back to the breath when we find ourselves lost in thought during meditation, the idea of returning to our positive mind, our daily affirmations and our ever-expanding consciousness builds our capacity for a peaceful, positive mind. I can't stress enough how much I cherish the moments when I find I have succumbed to fear or the moment when I realize I am judging myself and others in a way that is not healthy for me. My goal in those instances is to be kind to myself and have a thankful, grateful moment that I was aware enough to realize -- and then come back to my center. It is that simple and something I refer to as "Self-Love"!

Positive Affirmations and Mantras are powerful practices and, in many cases, rooted in the same garden of desires in our lives. I use Mantras as an easy phrase of my intentions that I can share with others. Think about words and phrases that resonate with the realization of your dreams. A couple examples are "I have perfect health" and "My body is healing perfectly". Together these can be a mantra such as "I have perfect health, my body is healing perfectly and I will grow through this experience." Come up with an affirmation or two, create a mantra or phrase and share them with your family and friends because this amplifies the power of our words. Always trust the process! **Consistency is key!**

CHAPTER 8
BLOG #7 | 3.25.14
The Next Phase of this Amazing Journey

Chapter Affirmation: **I create a chorus of positivity within my tribe.**

Hello friends!

I am so happy to report that I am writing this blog post from my condo and it feels so damn good to be home! After being away from home for 4.5 weeks, just being in my home, surrounded by my things, smelling my smell and sleeping in my bed is doing amazing things for me! I can't say enough great things about my friends who hosted me but damn, it feels good to be home! :)

I have been thinking a lot about this blog post b/c it is an important one...ok, ok...the salesman in me wants you to believe that every post is important (and they are all an important part of my journey) but today's post will explain the next phase of this amazing journey I am on!

Here is how I have been telling some of my friends...

1. My doctors tell me that I am going to live a long and healthy life and that it will likely be 60 years before my tumor tries to grow back (the type of tumor I had likes to come back).

2. I have a very rare form of brain tumor with two specific genetic mutations that put me in the minority of the minority...but this is A GOOD THING (I will explain later in this blog)

3. I do have brain cancer!

4. My doctors tell me that I am going to live a long and healthy life and that it will likely be 60 years before my tumor tries to grow back (the type of tumor I had likes to come back). I put this in again, so you would trust me! :)

5. My surgeon removed the entire tumor and they consider it a "perfect resection" ...this is amazing news!

6. I am going to start a 15-month treatment program that is all about PREVENTATIVE MAINTENANCE so that the tumor doesn't come back. The reason that we are doing this is b/c the doctors know that there is still cell growth in my brain that you can't see on an MRI or with your eye and thus treatment.

OK...take a deep breathe...or three.... seriously...I am in a great place with this and am going to live a really long and healthy life and kick cancer's ass...I promise! :)

Alrighty then.... that was a lot of information...trust me, I know...I have been working to wrap my head around it (haha) for the past two weeks and wanted to wait for the right moment to tell you about this! Before we go on...take another deep breath...it really helps!

The next phase of my journey or as we will call it, "treatment" will likely begin on April 2nd and will last for the better part of 15 months. The first phase of treatment will be a 6.5-week radiation and chemotherapy regimen that will involve taking chemotherapy pills every day and going to Vanderbilt every day (Monday-Friday) for radiation. The doctors have stressed that most patients do not have bad side effects from these two treatments and they fully expect me to "sail through" treatment! There is a chance that I will have some nausea from the chemotherapy and possibly a cumulative fatigue from the radiation. This is where the phrase *"my body responds perfectly to treatment comes in!"* That being said, I fully expect to be feeling great! :) After this 6.5-week treatment, I will take 1 month off and will then begin a 12-month chemotherapy regimen taking pills for one week, then three weeks off...repeated for 12 months! During the entire treatment process, I will be monitored closely and will hopefully be able to return to work once we all feel comfortable that I can and that my body is responding perfectly! :)

So, let's talk about some details for a second...it gets really technical really quickly so bear with me! ;)

I have learned that 1% of the world's cancer population has brain cancer and out of that 1% I am a minority b/c of the two genetic mutations that my cells have. More specifically, that my cancer/tumor cells have. I will talk more about these mutations as I learn more but for now I know about one of them and that is called the "co-deleted 1P19Q." What this means is that the remaining tumor cells that are in my body do not fight back against treatment...this is amazing news! One of the amazing things about our bodies is that we fight off infection, foreign invaders, germs, etc. and most of the time this is exactly what we want our bodies to do.... but apparently not when we are treating cancer! I say this b/c having a co-deleted 1P19Q means that my tumor cells do not fight back against the radiation and chemotherapy...again, this is a very good thing! My doctors told me that 10 years ago they didn't know about this mutation and that they only found it b/c they noticed that a segment of patients in some clinical trials/studies/etc. were living WAY longer than most patients and in many cases longer than the trials tracked patients. Learning about this made me feel really great, b/c I know that amazing people are constantly working on improving medical care and we can all rest easy knowing that this continues today.

OK...so now what?

Well, for me I am continuing to settle back into my home, resting, relaxing, writing in my journal, meditating daily and taking in every ounce of this experience that I have been blessed with! I am also going to be doing another MRI Thursday b/c my doctors told me that when they started to plan out my radiation treatment they were very pleasantly surprised to see that there was a BIG difference between the CT scan I did last week and the MRI I had the morning after surgery. The difference is b/c I am healing really well and the "cavity" in my brain (where the tumor was) has gotten much smaller (b/c it is healing so well) which means less area to treat with radiation and as result less risk to me...this also means I get to do another MRI! Once I am finished with the MRI, my doctors and their team will get back to the business of planning my radiation treatment and I should be able to start this next Wednesday (4/2/14)!

I want you all to know that I am in a good place with this and that I continue to be WAY more excited about the future than I am nervous! I continue to feel so lucky to be able to go through this experience and am so thankful for the love and support that all of you continue to give me... whether that is your sweet notes and cards, meals, rides, hugs, phone calls, etc....I am thankful that you are all in my life and truly appreciate you! I know that hearing the news that your friend has cancer can be scary...hell, when I first heard about this it was hard to keep my breath. The important thing that I want you all to know is that I will beat this, I am in a great place with all of this and the future is very, very bright! So now, one more time.... take a deep breathe...ahhhh...that feels good!
Thanks again for all of your support!

Justin

Reflecting Back:
Well...that post is a big one, right? Certainly, a post that I never anticipated writing and it gave me chills when I read it last week, after at least 3 years since my last read.

I am smiling because within these sentences are fearful emotions, confident emotions, grateful emotions and certainly my goal of managing everyone else's anxiety about what I was going through. In the two months before this post, I had quickly realized the importance of helping my friends and family be more at peace about my journey. Simply stated, when anxious/nervous people were around me, I could feel it and it wasn't a good feeling. Don't get me wrong, I knew that their love for me was at the root of their nervous and fearful emotions, but I didn't want to feel their tension...or perhaps I knew I should try to minimize it the best that I could so that I could still honor them where they are. Either way, I started communicating in an honest way that managed the news in a self-care, self-loving way.

I believe this is very important for all of us to think about because our tribe (friends/family), as I lovingly refer to them can be a part of the "chorus of positivity" that we create. However, it also can negatively impact our journey by projecting their own fears, anxieties, etc. onto our lives. By creating this chorus of positivity, we are able to multiply the positive energy and focus on our desired outcome, in my case "healing perfectly" and later, during chemo "my body is responding perfectly to treatment". This helped me so much! Every single person in my tribe was using the same language around me and focusing on the same outcomes. Not just surviving surgery but for me, it was a picture of me waking up in the recovery room, flirting with the nurses, and being fully aroused.

This is important because what this was really saying to my mind was that:
1. I will survive surgery
2. I will have my personality b/c I am a natural flirt...and they opened up my brain which could have significantly impacted my brain function
3. I will not be paralyzed from the waist down which was a risk based on where the tumor was in my brain.

Boom...the first Facebook post that my dad made on my page the day of my surgery was:

"This is Justin's dad. He's out of surgery and joking with the nurses. Surgeon says it went superb, actually routine."

It worked and would continue to work as I coached my tribe on how I wanted to talk about things and about how I saw things happening in my life. Honoring who they are and where they are and most importantly, honoring where I was and what I needed for myself. Self-Love my friends!

Our friends and families are important and so are the words that they say around us and the energy and emotions that we feel from them. You can help both of these areas support your healing journey with two easy steps. First, create a consistent chorus of positivity within your tribe by sharing the vision you are working to create and the words that you use to talk about your journey. This will empower your tribe to support you with consistent positive language and imagery while you magnify the manifesting power of your mind through the process of sharing with the people that are closest to you. The next step is to communicate information about your journey in a way that prioritizes your experience by helping reduce the shock factor and anxiety that these types of conversations can cause in the people close to you. Having the same tough conversation, multiple times can be draining and approaching these experiences from a place of self-love, with a focus on your experience, will help minimize the negative impacts that these conversations can have on your life.

CHAPTER 9
BLOG #8 | 4.3.14
1 Down, 32 To Go!

Chapter affirmation: **My breath calms me. I honor every moment of my life. My life's journey is divinely guided.**

That's right folks, 1 down and 32 to go! My treatment started today, and I am glad to be on the other side of my "day 1". Now, this is not b/c today was physically painful in any way and certainly not because the Vanderbilt staff were anything other than their consistent level of amazingness-seriously, I am continuously impressed by this hospital! I am glad to be on the other side for a few reasons...first of all, I was nervous and a little anxious about starting treatment. I am also glad that we have started treatment b/c the sooner we start...THE SOONER WE FINISH!! :) As far as my health is concerned, the doctors have told me that the ideal window to start this radiation/chemo combination is 4-6 weeks from surgery and 4/3/14 is 6 weeks from surgery-great timing, score 1 for the home team! :)

I said that today wasn't physically painful, but I had been anticipating today's start of treatment and that naturally caused a little bit of anxiety with an overwhelming sense of "Come on, let's get this going and kick ass!" This anxiety was not at all about the long-term future but more about the upcoming treatment and the unknown. I have been meditating daily, being very positive and yet when I laid down on the table today I was nervous. Fear my friends, I know this is totally normal and if I wasn't a little nervous/anxious something would be wrong with me...dare I say, "harboring/burying some emotions"! :) Seriously though, I breathed through my anxiety by focusing on my breath and actually counting it. I learned this method in the daily meditations I have been doing every morning. I am sure I will talk more about this once I learn more but, basically, once you are relaxed, 1st observe your breath as it is normally. The next step is to count every inhale and exhale...inhale (1), exhale (2), etc. etc. until you get to 10 and then repeat. To be honest, I jumped right to the counting today on the table b/c I was nervous! :) haha...sometimes I have to laugh at myself! The moral of this story is that once again, I felt anxiety, came close to being overwhelmed (while I was on the table) and took it back to the breath...it works!

Starting this next phase which, my dad labeled today as "Phase 3" is exciting! We are starting the part of this story that will ensure this cancer doesn't come back and a phase that will certainly continue to teach me more about myself, my amazing friends and family and likely some more medical terms. I have learned a TON over the past 8.5 weeks! My doctor and nurse friends tell me they are impressed with my new medical terminology...I say I just want to know what is going on with my body! I can't help but love data...especially when my health is involved! :) Having the chemotherapy pills in my possession for the past 3-4 weeks has felt kinda weird...maybe weird isn't the right word but for lack of a better word, we will use it! It has been the ever-constant reminder of the next phase of this journey and also of where I am in my life.... basically, a consistent "it's real" hanging around! You know me well enough by now to know that I take it for what it is and totally own where I am in the experience...just an interesting observation that I have had lately. When I took the first dose I remember the nervous and excited feelings as I held them in my hands and used it as a good time to set a positive intention and focus on emerging healthier and happier than ever! :) But just so we know we are keeping it real, I was nervous...or maybe just anxious...hell, or both...but either way...it was a big moment in my life and this journey!

(Continued the following day) -----I'm not sure what I felt, when I felt it and what caused it, but I didn't feel 100% all day yesterday! I never really felt horrible, but I think that the combination of the emotions, meds and just the anticipation of that day had EVERYTHING to do with it! Today (Day 2) is already feeling good and I am looking forward to a great day today! It doesn't take much for me to reflect on just how lucky I am to be sitting here (and that you are reading this:)) and I find myself reflecting on this all the time! Working to max out life has always been a part of my life and thankfully I have amazing friends around me that work to do the same...birds of a feather flocking together I suppose! When we all lost our dear friend and brother Alan last June it shook us and then when we found out our friend Jacoby needed a kidney it shook us again and then when this story started it shook us again...and sadly when a friend of ours took his own life last Sunday it shook us again! I know that everyone will grow from these life experiences in personal ways and that is awesome! The only thing I would want to put on a billboard or put out there as a key theme that I focus on, is to work to live the life that you truly love, that makes you happy and fulfilled and to just keep things positive! :)

Thanks again for all of your support and love and for reading this blog! I finally got around to redirecting my domain world, so in the future you can always go to www.justinlevenson.com (or subscribe to get email notifications). Going forward, I may even get crazy and try to get some help with art or some graphics...look out friends!

Here's to a great day!

Justin

Reflecting Back:
Ah, a post from the official two-month mark from the day I had the seizure...I can almost feel my heart thump like it was yesterday...only it was just short of seven years ago! Fear, anxiety, nerves...all are beautiful

59

reminders that we are alive. Yes, in these instances I was alive to face more experiences that caused unpleasant reminders, but I was alive none the less. I was alive, and I was grateful, and I knew there would be better days in my future.

These were the first two days of chemotherapy and radiation at Vanderbilt and for those that are wondering what radiation is like for the brain, do a quick web search on radiation masks and you will see what I was talking about (or look at page 62 of this book - that's my radiation mask). Basically, imagine yourself on a small, metal medical table, underneath a large machine. Next imagine a custom-made mask that fits snuggly on your face as you lay on your back on this table, waiting for the nurse to fasten the mask, and thus your body, to the table. Yeah.... whoa...I am really glad that whole phase is over! Regardless of how prepared I thought I was, or wasn't, I felt lucky that I was able to use the meditation tools that I had just learned over the previous couple of months to help me be more at peace. This was a divinely guided chain of events that was so right on time...so right on time!

I can still remember how intense it was to have my chemotherapy pills arrive at my house-my treatment was all via capsules versus a port or IV. The feeling of opening up that box from Cigna, to find three large plastic bottles, with a fancy pharmaceutical name right underneath my full name. All of a sudden, my life took another leap down the road of "this is real Justin" and it definitely took a few days, if not weeks to really sink in, and for me to find peace with it all. Right around this time, I started videoing myself and doing what I now call my "video journals" and I have my first chemotherapy dose recorded. After recently watching all of my video journals for the first time, this day really sticks out to me b/c you can feel my anxiety and nerves and also watch me work to keep my mind focused on the positive while owning the reality of that moment. Powerful moments, caught on tape, showing all sides of my journey, that I will be sharing in the months and years to come.

I truly believe it is important for us to honor all of the moments in our journey and especially the painful moments because so far in my life, the extremes are where the extreme growth is waiting for me... and is likely where it is waiting for you too. Moments that are waiting for us with loving patience to feel deeply, love ourselves deeply and just be our most honest, open and truthful selves. Waiting for us to grow through the moments, not grow around them. This post shows me working to do all of that and thankfully these are all still focuses of my life today. Feeling through my emotions versus getting over them...a theme that rings truer today than ever before.

Whether you call it meditation or counting or something else, simple breathing exercises can help you reduce anxiety and increase feelings of calm and relaxation. The breathing exercise I used on the radiation table is simple. If you can count to 10, you can try it right now. Begin by finding a comfortable place to sit down, gently close your eyes, and begin to observe your breath. As you observer your breath, start counting your breathing on an inhale with "1", and your exhale "2", inhale "3", exhale "4", continued until you reach 10 and then repeat for as long as you want...or until you calm down a little bit. You can use this technique anywhere and anytime. When you find that you are lost in thought, and not counting your breathing, lovingly bring your mind back to the breath and begin counting again! And trust me, every time I do this I get lost in thought. Your breath is a powerful tool my friends.

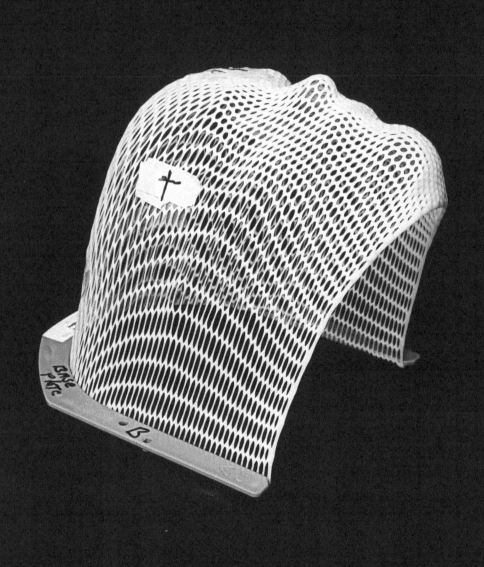

CHAPTER 10
BLOG #9 | 4/21/14
I Am Going to Have a High-Tech Head.

Chapter affirmation: **I welcome this radiation into my body, to fulfill the promise of eradicating cancer from my body and I am thankful for those who administer it.**

That's right friends, my head and hell, my whole body has some high-tech treatment going on right now! Today was my 12th radiation treatment and the 16th day taking the chemo pills which means I am more than a third of the way done! Whoop Whoop! :) The treatment is getting easier every time. I'm not saying that it is exactly fun yet (ok... it probably won't ever be "fun") but it is definitely getting easier every day! It also helps when I think about this helping me live a very long and healthy life! The chemo still makes me feel "meh" and the Zofran anti-nausea med is my friend for sure...that said, it is manageable and when I feel like resting...I rest! Every day when I take my chemo I set two intentions that help me have more peace through this and they are "my body responds perfectly to treatment" and "I will emerge healthier, happier and more empowered to do great things". I set these intentions, throw back the pills and a glass of water and that daily, consistent dose of positivity turns taking the meds into something that helps me have peace! The radiation treatment is all a mental thing...100% a mental thing! I mentioned that I made a mask before treatment and I wear this every day, as it is attached to the table I am laying on. We do this to keep my head in exactly the same place during the radiation treatment.

OK...in full disclosure...I started this blog on Thursday, April 17th, 2014 and fully intended to finish that day...but I didn't! Today is Monday, April 21st, 2014 and there is no sexy, adventurous story that I can tell you about why I didn't finish this post. The simple, true story is that I haven't really felt like it and wasn't feeling 100% towards the end of last week and over the weekend! I haven't been feeling horrible and what I am feeling is totally manageable, but I definitely wasn't feeling great! My nausea is pretty well under control with the meds. At this point, it is more just a sense of not feeling like myself, at times a little tired and just "meh"! I have been thinking about wanting to finish this post and keep pushing myself to be active, etc. and after a good night's sleep last night, I am feeling great today! It is almost time to take my daily dose of chemo and go rock out radiation treatment #14 shortly! This week is full of appointments at Vanderbilt and spending time with friends which sounds like a great week to me! I saw all four of my doctors last week and they are all pleased with how I am healing and handling the treatment! My surgeon saw me for the first time since being in the hospital two months ago and it was great to see him and be able to deliver the "Super J" t-shirts to him and Tracy. They rock!

So... back to the radiation treatment! Like I mentioned, I wear the mask to keep my head in the same place so that they can get the radiation exactly where they want it...apparently within a millimeter...so cool! I lay down on a little table, get situated with some pads under my knees and ankles (the table is not made for tall people) :) and prepare to have the mask put on me and connected to the table! Thanks to someone that works at Sony that had treatment or some Sony connection, there is a stack of Sony Nashville artist CD's that I listen to which helps me relax... yep, I said it...pop country helping me relax! :) hahaha! Once they get me lined up perfectly, they take a few "positioning x-rays" to make sure I am lined up and then the treatment starts. The machine moves around my head and stops at five different positions to shoot radiation based on the best way to target the right spots and stay away from critical parts of my brain...thanks team, I appreciate that! :). I haven't counted with any exact measurements, but my guess is that I am on the table for about

10-15 minutes and in actual radiation a total of about a minute every day! Treatment is certainly getting easier every day and with that said, at times I still take it back to counting my breath when I am on the table! This practice helps me and is something I continue to expand on in my daily meditations (that are really going well and I'm really enjoying the practice). Being an observer vs. a judger/fixer/etc. is helping me have a greater sense of peace and I welcome it! I am still using the Head Space website/app. This daily practice is working! :)

The awesome team that administers the radiation helps me every day! They have all been just as amazing as everyone else at Vanderbilt and make me feel very comfortable. Part of what makes my treatment get easier every day is my growing relationship, and thus my comfort with these women! Many things are changing as a result of this journey, and I am excited about that but me being a people person and thriving off personal relationships rings truer than ever! :)

I don't think I ever contemplated knowing about technology like this but damn, I am really glad it exists! One of the therapists said something like "We are hiding out down here in the basement (of the building) and are the folks nobody ever wants to know about...but when they find out about us, they are really glad that we are here!" I couldn't say it better myself because I am so thankful that they are here and that I continue to have access to such amazing medical care! When I have had low moments over the past couple of weeks having a sense of gratitude has really helped me! Thinking about how thankful I am to be alive to experience these feelings and emotions and being thankful that I have the ability to go through these high-tech treatments that are going to ensure that I live a very long and healthy life! This is amazing and well worth a few weeks of not quite feeling 100%!!

Here's to all of us having a great week full of amazing people and experiences!

Justin

Reflecting Back:

Well, the mask...I told you it was intense and my words in this blog post about it continue to reinforce the ups and downs of my experience with the 33 radiation treatments I received. I certainly don't miss being restrained to a small, metal table by a tight-fitting mask and at the same time I am grateful I had access to such amazing medical care. The part of this post that really makes me smile today is the positivity and the gratefulness that I feel from my words in this blog post. Being grateful is such a powerful thing for all of us, especially when we are able to have a grateful thought, in the midst of anxious, fearful, or stressful emotions. This immediately helps us re-center and start reducing those negative emotions. Ultimately, creating more peace in our day and using the power of our breath and intentional positive, grateful feelings to improve our experience.

This post also demonstrates my continued use of the main positive mantra that I used throughout my cancer treatment and was the first time that I shared it with the world via this blog post. I also want to point out the positive affirmation that I used during some of my radiation treatments and that is the affirmation referenced above. "I welcome this radiation into my body, to fulfill the promise of eradicating cancer from my body and I am thankful to those that administer it". Using this affirmation helped me reduce anxiety and send positive messages to my mind in the midst of a very stressful experience.

When these blog posts were first published, they were public, and shared via email and social media. While my blog was initially my public way to manage news and communicate with the community, it grew into a form of self-expression and a helpful resource for others on their own healing journey. Almost two weeks before I wrote this blog post, I began a separate, more private healing practice of creating video journals of my experiences. In fact, I haven't stopped recording video journals to document my continued healing. At first the idea of talking to my cell phone video camera felt a little cheesy and I questioned it. I wasn't sure it felt like "me", but I figured I would give it a try. Wow! I am so happy that I took my friend Marc's advice and started creating a video documentation of my healing journey. I have captured so many impactful moments over the past seven years and look forward to sharing more of them in the future.

Here is my first ever video journal from one of the early days of chemotherapy where I used my main positive mantra to affirm positively to my subconscious mind, while also helping me reduce the anxiety I was feeling. I used this mantra throughout my cancer journey and always encouraged my tribe to focus on this picture!

You can create powerful mantras too and they will help you and your tribe be intentional with the way that you speak about your life. If you haven't already created your own mantra, revisit chapter 7 and think about your goals and intentions. These will help you create a short and impactful mantra to repeat throughout your day and to share with your family and friends. The more you think, speak, feel and share this mantra, the more powerful it becomes!

www.justinlevenson.com/strongerthanyouthink

When you see images similar to the code (left), simply view the image with your cell phone camera (or visit the website link directly) to watch a small collection of videos that correspond with the timeline of this book.

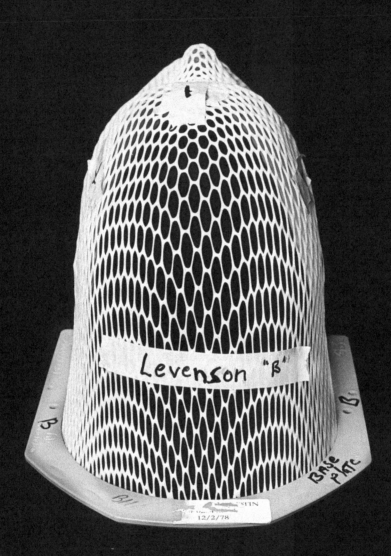

Levenson "B"

BASE PLATE

12/2/78

CHAPTER 11
BLOG #10 | 5.7.14
My Body is Responding Perfectly!

Chapter affirmation: **My body is responding perfectly to treatment. Creating and repeating impactful thoughts and words helps me throughout my journey.**

Hello from Nashville on a beautiful May morning on 2nd Avenue! It has been another great couple of weeks in my world and the treatment is still getting easier every day! Today will be my 26th radiation treatment which means I will have 7 more after today! Today starts what they are calling the "boost" and I have no idea what that means other than my "treatment" will change a little bit and maybe a stronger treatment in a smaller space...I think I remember hearing something about that! I will fill you in! What I do know is that I get to spend a few extra minutes in my mask today which will be fun... :) Seriously, it has gotten much more relaxed for me during treatment and although I won't miss having to wear the mask in the future, I can totally handle the remaining treatments with me, my breath and usually some country music (one of my friends there loves the song "Hot Mess" by Tyler Farr and plays it often and I'll admit, it has grown on me...doesn't hurt that she proclaims that it is her "theme song"!)

My Chemo is still doing its thing and I will enjoy a break from this too, although as you know, I will be taking it 5 days per month for the next 12 months (likely June-June I think). The chemo doesn't hit my stomach as hard as it did at first, but I certainly can tell I take it as it makes me just not feel great...that said, it is time for me to take it now...one second!

Well alright, that was easy...and yes, I still do my vocal intentions every day...I even recorded a few of them to document it in living color!

Many people have asked me how I have been feeling and the best way I can describe it is that "I am feeling about 80% BUT am 100% ALIVE!" The radiation started to make me feel a little fatigued a couple weeks ago and that has grown over time, like the doctors said it would. It doesn't make me immobile, but it certainly makes me want a nap... for example, yesterday I took two naps during the day so that I could have some energy for yoga! Yes, yoga...I finally practiced since all of this started thanks to my neighbor Betsy who has a Zen yoga studio in her condo! It was great to stretch, breathe and move together and I can't wait to do it again! Back to the treatment, the radiation is almost done and that is the real story because, whatever I am feeling, I can make it through next Friday easily! With the combination of chemo and the fatigue from the radiation I have not been that active compared to what my mind wants to do but per my doctors, I am more active than most patients and doing really well! They are encouraging me to stay active and balance the desire to push through the fatigue with resting... **basically, listen to your body and give it what it needs!**

My growing love affair with having my blood taken (laugh) is really getting much better as I become more comfortable with something that I will have to do pretty often for the rest of my life. I celebrated not passing out the past two times...seriously! hahaha! I get blood work done every two weeks because they watch certain levels very closely to make sure **my body is responding perfectly to treatment**, and if need be, make changes! I am happy to report that my first two blood work results came back "perfect" and my doctors couldn't be happier about it! My body is truly responding "perfectly" to treatment...awesome!

As part of the perfect response, I am also losing a little hair in the spots where the radiation is directed, which the doctors said was possible! There is one spot in the front, middle of my head (yup) and one on the left side of my head. All of my hair will grow back 100% and now we get to play a game I like to call "What color and texture will my hair grow back?"...stay tuned for updates here! :) I quickly named the front my "soul patch" and the other my "soul side" but those names haven't stuck yet, and I welcome suggestions. What if I got a blonde, curly soul patch right in the front...whoa!!! hahaha!

I have some more good news for all of us to celebrate too. My great friend Jacoby, who we mention at the bottom of this page has been looking for a kidney donor b/c she is in serious need of a new kidney and SHE FOUND ONE!!!! Her awesome cousin Mills is donating one of his kidneys and they have a surgery scheduled for the week after next! Please send some positive energy and prayers to both of them and the hospital staff and envision a "perfect procedure" for them! This is also happening at Vanderbilt which is part of why I have such a sense of peace about this procedure...it will be great! Our friends have set up an opportunity to help Jacoby and her cousin with some of the financial needs that come with being out of work, surgery, medicine, etc. If you are in a position to help or know others that may be, please check this link out. At the very least, send out some love please! :)

Well, it is about time for Romero to show up to hang for a second and then take me to treatment, so I will stop this one here! I have much more to share with you and will get another blog up sometime soon! I hope things are going well in your world!

Have a great day!

Justin

Reflecting Back:

Well, thankfully my hair grew back completely, and I never had to fully own the less than cool names of "soul patch" and "soul side" but I am really glad to read them here. It makes me happy because I am reading laughter and me being a little funny in this post and considering what my physical body was going through during this time, I am really proud of myself to have been able to keep it real...both in the intense, anxious parts and in the part that speaks from my personality, which always tries to have a joyous smile somewhere close by!

The story behind the story of the blood work is that I used to be the biggest baby when it came to needles...seriously...I would get so nervous at my annual physicals. By this point in the cancer journey, I clearly was celebrating getting more used to this...and to be 100% transparent, I quietly celebrated the same thing two weeks ago at my four-month checkup with the oncology team-side note, I am really healthy and staying on the four-month follow up schedule! Woo Hoo!

The title of this blog entry "My Body is Responding Perfectly" is something I really want to talk about. As you know, I really believe strongly in the power of my subconscious mind to not only improve my experience today and also to plant intentional, powerful seeds of positivity inside my mind. These are certainly a large part of my daily practice of positive affirmations, which continue today, and they are also evident in many other areas of my life. I seriously try to speak them, write them, think them, share them and live them as much as I can. I want these affirmations, these goals, to be so ever present in my life that there is no way I can't live them. The more these affirmations are present, the more impressions they make on my mind, the more I feel their calming, positive, and nurturing energy and the more impactful they become in my life experience.

In this blog post, I am driving home the key affirmation that I was focusing on at this time which was that "my body is responding perfectly to treatment". By sharing this affirmation directly and indirectly with my tribe, I feel that I am magnifying the love, the positivity and the power of these thoughts and words. This is something that we can all do today, whether we are fighting a disease, working to overcome something in our personal or professional life or working to support people that we love. When our tribe speaks and thinks in line with our goals and affirmations, our bodies and souls are nourished on overdrive. And when I wrote and now read this post from this point in my cancer journey, I am struck by the chorus of my goal and my intention to share the message with my tribe that my body is responding perfectly to treatment. This is powerful now and for the rest of our days in this life. Through this technique of creating repeating, impactful thoughts and words, we are able to help ourselves and our loved ones through any experience that we face.

We all have bad days and going through cancer means that having a bad day is practically a given. Own these moments and know that you are allowed to have as many bad days as you desire. I also want you to know that you have the power to shift things in those moments too; and sometimes a good laugh and smile can make a big impact. When you laugh and smile, you release endorphins and reduce the stress hormone cortisol which makes you feel happier and less stressed. Said another way, simply being able to bring a smile to your face or having a funny thought and a laugh will help you reduce stress and increase your happiness. Give this a try the next time you could use a positive shift in your day.

I think it is important for you to find as many opportunities to laugh and smile as you can (even if it's about a new bald spot on our heads!). Here are a few videos that show the progression of hair loss and my positive attitude. This is me, honoring where I am, trusting that my body is responding perfectly and being open to every new experience that comes my way.

www.justinlevenson.com/strongerthanyouthink

CHAPTER 12
BLOG #11 | 5.16.14
The End of An Era

Chapter affirmation: **I am loved, supported and cared for. I welcome love into my life in every way.**

Hi friends! It's another beautiful day in the neighborhood here on 2nd avenue! (It is Thursday afternoon, 5/15/14) Ok...in full disclosure, it is a little partly cloudy with more rain on the way...but the vibe in my condo is about as happy as I have been since the night before this whole thing started, partying with my neighbors at a Super Bowl Party! I'm happy because my 6.5-week, intense radiation/chemo treatments are less than 24 hours away from being finished!! YES! :) And from a bigger view perspective, the past 3.5 months have been pretty intense from 2/3/14 on. I certainly have more treatment to go over the next 13-14 months, but it is fair to say that the first 3.5 months have been the most negatively intense of this entire experience, and hopefully for the rest of my life! The past 3.5 months have taken us from a seemingly normal Monday to the ER after a big seizure at the office, to a perfect brain surgery (craniotomy if you care to know the real name), to a cancer diagnosis and the big chunk of intense treatments to make sure it doesn't come back for a long time. I went from worrying about my parent's health and thinking about ways to help our whole family be healthier to personally looking death in the eye while I anticipated dealing with a surgery and whatever post-surgery news (pathology of my tumor, etc.) would bring and it was something that at times, seemed more than I could handle! But you know what? It was never more than I could handle...

ever! No matter how scared I was, no matter how anxious I felt at times, no matter how emotional I felt...and no matter how many moments I questioned if I was about to freak out, it was never more than I could handle! Hell, yesterday on the radiation table I was anxious for some reason and it was my 30th treatment. I don't try to judge it at this point and just try to observe the ebb and flow of my emotions. Yesterday, I seriously counted my breath and thought "this is helping me live a long and healthy life" and then envisioned myself having lunch and laughing afterwards! My point is that the past 3.5 months have been amazingly intense...absolutely amazingly intense and so overwhelmingly positive. They have also provided moments of worry, anxiety and loneliness and when I reflect on the 3.5 months as a whole, I see that I was provided such amazing opportunities to grow and learn about myself, my family, my friends and the amazing community around me! I feel so lucky that I have had this opportunity to have a perspective reset on my life...the future is very exciting! :)

I have always been in awe of Nashville's heart. Yeah, we love our tourism, our healthcare and our music industry...but we really love our friends and our fellow Nashvillians and we take care of each other!! I am thankful that I have had the opportunity to be on the giving side of Nashville's amazing nonprofit community for many years, but this was my first experience to be on the receiving end of that community love and it blew me away! Seriously, when I first started feeling the love flow into me before surgery I was speechless...it was overwhelming from an emotional place! Thank you! I always knew that giving back, helping and teaching people and touching the universe were things that made me joyful, but to say I have an increased passion for this now is quite the understatement! :) Just as I started to feel like thinking about something other than myself and my day, new opportunities to give back started flooding my realm so look out...I'm fired up to turn my life experiences into as many opportunities to do great things as I can!

Alright friends, I'm back...and it's Friday, my last day of radiation and my last day taking chemo for a month!!! Wooo Hooo! I thought I would share my current view that I am always so thankful for! It is a beautiful day in Nashville today with a little chill in the air, great tunes coming through my speakers, I just FaceTime'd with my mom and good friend Brit (who is sitting on the beach...jealous) and I am about to get a 90-minute massage!! Oh, and did I mention it is the last time I get to be held down on a table by a tight-fitting mask? hahaha! :) After treatment I am going to let the awesome ladies at the salon help me figure out what to do with my hair now that I can get it cut. The real question is do I grow it out to cover the soul patch up front (my little bald spot) or cut it pretty short and rock the easy, buzz all summer? Decisions, decisions...but really.... who cares, it's only hair!!!

I am alive and am wrapping up the first 3.5 months of this amazing journey and starting the next phase which is a month of rest to let my body recover and heal! Ah....

Another reason I love my view of Nashville is because I get to see growth all around me and have been able to watch our city grow up over the past 12 years from my little sliver of town on 2nd Avenue! I can't help but think of metaphors like growing up with the town over as many years and also about our cities bright future ahead because I know my future is very bright too! Through this entire experience I have remained WAY more excited about the future than I was scared and most of my nerves and anxiety were about the unknown, the tomorrow, the start of treatment, THE MASK, etc.! :) As I look out over a beautiful growing Nashville, I am happy to be able to see myself growing with it. I have certainly grown with it over the past 14 years of living in Middle TN, and over the past 12 years of owning a little piece of it and wow...I have certainly been able to see myself grow over the past 3.5 months! I think it really started (or I started remembering it) when the 5 doctors came into my ER room to tell me I had a brain tumor. I remember having an immediate sense of peace rush over my body and I proceeded to tell the doctors about how I was going to turn this into the most amazingly positive experience of my life and help so many people through this experience. It was this sense of peace, that I immediately felt, that has stayed with me at my core -no matter how anxious I felt in the moment- and I continue to visualize myself at peace in the future! I believe this was and is a direct result of the seeds of positivity that my parents planted in me at a young age and that I nurtured and fell in love with as I became an adult! I have such vivid memories of my dad tucking me in at night and saying, "repeat after me boychik...through the power of my subconscious mind, I ward off all evil, I have perfect health...!" Thanks Mom and Dad! :)

Well, I just realized that it is 9:00 and I need to get my day going! I hope you all have an awesome day and weekend! Thank you all for the support and love you have shown my family and me during the past 3.5 months! I love you and look forward to seeing you all soon!

Justin

Reflecting Back:
Growth. This is the word that just popped in my head after reading this post today...growth of self...growth of my heart...growth of my love for myself...I am grateful! I hope that you can feel my excitement and positivity as in this post as you read my words, I know I can.

The next word that this post brings to my mind is Love. For years before this specific cancer journey started in early 2014, I held love at a distance in my personal life. I often thought about how I didn't want "drama" or didn't want "to have to report into someone about my life" and plenty of other thoughts that kept me from being open to love. This really had more to do with intimate relationships and where I was and when the amazing community of Nashville found out about my seizure and surgery, their love burst down the walls I had built around my heart. This love was intense and being a guy that always seems to have something to say, I was speechless. Seriously speechless. I couldn't find a word to describe the swelling in my chest that was love. This inability to wrap my mind around it was a beautiful gift because it points directly at my heart, which is the area that really needed healing. Feeling and not thinking is what I am talking about. Listening to my heart's desire for love, without letting my mind, and the fear it spoke with, convince me to run from love. I didn't know what I needed but I knew how great it felt and once I got over the uncomfortable feeling of being helped, needing support, etc. I welcomed every ounce of love from my community. And trust me, when I say community, I am not just talking about the friends that brought me food, took me to treatments and sent cards. I am talking about the thousands of people all over the world that were reading my blogs, sending love my way and keeping me in their prayers. Whether I heard from them directly or not does not matter because I felt so much loving energy in every part of my life. Thank you! I am equally grateful now as I was certainly overwhelmed with gratitude then.

What I later realized is that I was not loving myself, and instead, I was spending more time judging myself than loving myself. This is why the idea of "Judge Less, Love More" was so right on the money when I had the thought in the early weeks of this journey. When I judge myself less and love myself more, I open myself to all of the amazing love the universe has for me (and for you). I say this because I firmly believe that until we love ourselves, we cannot truly be available to love someone else...or certainly not enough to bring in the kind of amazing souls we all hope to have or do have in our lives. This post is the first one of this blog that really speaks to me loving myself more in ways that show growth to me. Just as I used the metaphor of Nashville's growth and my own in this blog post, the same metaphor continues to ring true today. It rings true because I have continued to love myself more, aka "grow" over the past seven years and this expanding love within my heart and soul has ushered in an amazing woman into my life who wouldn't have been interested in the closed off, single, "running from love" version of myself.

This expanding self-love has also helped me be able to carry love and compassion out to the world as I prepare to publish this book and begin releasing more content in the months and years to come. Loving myself more has allowed me to love others more and loving others more has helped me live a more balanced and fulfilled life for which I am incredibly grateful! Cheers to Love and cheers to growth...I welcome more into my life with every passing second!

I love to celebrate life...and the end to the combined chemotherapy and radiation therapy that I went through. Your life is to be celebrated! Seriously, life can be stressful, and some days are just not easy. When you find yourself having one of these days, or even just one of these moments, take a few moments to celebrate being alive to experience it (that whole gratitude thing again). Here is a celebratory video from the last chemo round of this intense combo treatment.

www.justinlevenson.com/strongerthanyouthink

CHAPTER 13
BLOG #12 | 6.25.14
And....I'm Back!

Chapter affirmation: **Everything in my life has prepared me for everything in it. My life feels amazing and grows peacefully every day. I welcome love, peace and prosperity into my life.**

Seriously...I'm back! Yes, I am back in regard to finally writing another blog post (thanks for those of you that have been asking about one) but what I really mean is that I (as in Justin, the author, J-Lev, etc. etc.) is back! Now there are several metaphors I can and will draw to being "back" but most importantly I feel that my body has made tremendous progress on the physical journey recovering from surgery and the intensive daily chemotherapy and radiation therapy! I feel better at this very moment, then I have felt all year long! My last treatment day was 5/16/14 and the past several weeks have been a welcome rest from what I see as the most negatively intense part of this journey. By the middle of May, I was pretty worn down and although my mind was positive, strong and confident in the end result; my body was feeling tired and it would have been very easy to focus on how weak I felt and how nauseous I felt! So that we still know we are keeping things real, the 6.5 weeks of treatment definitely were not a blast, it definitely made me feel pretty rough at times...but you know what....it wasn't THAT bad, and I made it through with a smile on my face! :) I truly believe this is a continuing result of the positive energy I was surrounded by and that I was working to generate in my core...and likely part of the larger spiritual journey I have been on for years! PLUS...have I mentioned that I seriously have some of the best doctors and medical staff in the world! (We are lucky in Nashville)

So, to get you updated medically, I saw my Oncologist and Radiologist last week after an early morning MRI and blood work. First of all, cheers to me for not passing out again when they set up the IV for the MRI! Woo Hoo! :) The MRI was no big deal at all after 6.5 weeks of that radiation mask and I almost fell asleep in the MRI twice! The doctors all thought the MRIs and my lab work looked great and said this is exactly how they expected me to progress (really really well)! The main point of the meeting was to talk about the next phase of my medical journey and that is the 12-month regimen of chemotherapy which has me taking Temodar pills (chemo) 5 days in a row per month. I started the first monthly round last night and will continue through May 2015. I am expecting this to go very well! It is twice the daily dose that I was taking before but ONLY for 5 days in row and I can take it right before I go to sleep to hopefully sleep through the peak of any potential side effects! The short story is that I'm kicking ass and between right now and May 2015 I have to be at Vanderbilt 6 times (every other month) for an MRI and to see my Oncologist and the other 6 months have to make arrangements to have lab work done the week before I start chemo (that they mail to me) :) I asked them when I can return to work and the general consensus was to wait for the first month of chemotherapy to get in my system and then also out of the my system the following weeks, etc. and go from there. With all of this said, I see myself being able to return to work by mid-July which will be awesome!

There you have it...I'm back physically, medically kicking ass and will soon be back to work...I love this! I am also getting back out socially which is feeling great! A large part of my balance in life is really about being around people, getting to know them, developing relationships with them and growing together! I am so excited to be getting back out in a social setting to enjoy my friends, meet new ones and really just enjoy more people! I may not drink alcohol any more, but I am all about some Sprite and darts at 1:30 AM with friends and although I don't drink in smoky karaoke bars by my house, I can still drink water and sing the hell 'outta some Sammy Kershaw...or hell, I'd even show off how "Fancy" I was (Iggy Azalea) ...my friend Britt will definitely approve! :) My point is that I am feeling like getting out more and more and have been doing just that, and it feels amazing!

As much as I want to tell you about how "back" I am, I think the most meaningful part of this journey is what isn't coming back with me...what is part of my "old normal"...the things I am working to grow through, soak up and really deal with...those things that only myself really know I think about and notice about myself...little things that I believe will help me be a better person and cultivate stronger and more meaningful relationships! Know that this self-examination has been underway for some time and through this and combined with my daily mediations and conversations with myself and friends; life is getting better by the moment! :)

"I love my new normal", "I don't want my old life back", "my life is forever changed in amazing ways, and I am just beginning to experience this growth...and will continue to for the rest of my life", "I am looking at the same amazing life, rooted in the same core of positivity and love... only now, through a new lens, a new perspective that has opened up a glorious new world, that was there the entire time", "the peace and connectedness I feel now, feels better than anything I have ever experienced...the feeling of walking the exact divinely guided path I am intended to walk...the feeling that everything in my life has prepared me for this moment...it is beautiful".

The quotes above are all things I say, talk about and think about often. This is how I feel and what makes me feel amazing! For so many years of my life, I have been motivated to get somewhere, something or someone...this is even as I was coaching other people and even working to coach myself about how we as humans should embrace every moment like it could be our last, while living to be healthy for the future!

I now feel a desire to maintain a feeling vs. achieve a status or job! This feeling of freedom, the feeling of connectedness and synchronicity, the feeling of love and centeredness...the feeling that my life is right where it is supposed to be, poised to do anything, go anywhere and touch the universe!! These, my friends, are some of the products of me spending much of the past 4 months alone in my home! This is what my "new normal" is centered in! Yes, I have the best family and so many amazing friends and they have all been an amazing support! But the majority of my time has been alone which is just how it was supposed to be... to provide this opportunity to center, to take it all in, to heal and to be sitting here today feeling more connected to the divine than I have ever been! The more that I surrender to this feeling and release myself to the journey, the better it feels, the more connected/synchronistic experiences appear and the more at peace I feel. I see it as a big snowball of increased consciousness and love that is building in me, around me with my friends and family and really as a community! I have found that most of my insecurities have come as a result of my own judgement of other people and I don't want to judge others nor feel the way it makes me feel. Being judgmental isn't healthy for me, even though I always thought that my simultaneous "loving person" qualities would overpower my judgements, they ultimately haven't and don't. I am a work in progress, and this is one area that I will be very mindful of going forward. Just being able to type these words feels so much lighter and makes me smile!

So yes friends, I am back! I'd like to call it new and improved and on the path of continuous improvement...aren't we all? The answer is yes... with a "but"...that's because we have to be open to experience it, to be open to it, to embrace it at all cost, to feel through it and to be open to trust it! Once we do, things begin to be easier and more peaceful, life gets deeper in "the pocket"! It feels awesome! I believe this feeling is infectious, energizing and within all of our respective powers to achieve!

Here's to continuing to grow together and feeling that feeling that makes each of us feel more alive than we could have imagined!

Justin

Reflecting Back:
Ah the joys of the upswings in life! We have all been there and we all know that the world also has a beautiful way of showing us the opposite end of that cycle... the down swings. These highs and lows are a natural part of life and I immediately think of nature and the four seasons as a basic example.

This post makes me think about the ups and downs, the peaks and valleys and the great days and bad days of my cancer journey. This was almost five months into this journey and my natural high is evident in every word I read above. The renewed energy and vitality are palpable inside me as I type these words today. After such an intense series of highs and lows over the previous months, being in that space of healing, with more energy than I had experienced in months was a new version of being alive for me. It was a simple reminder to myself that I was indeed moving in the perfect direction for myself, as my body, mind and spirit were healing in big ways. Even today, I smile because I know I am still healing and the trend line that I started after surgery is continuing in full force in my life! My energetic, positive attitude at this time is also interesting to me because I had no idea what the future was going to feel like and that doesn't matter. What I did know was that I was growing, healing and loving myself more than I ever had. I was working to be open and being very vulnerable and open to the world in the process. I love this post for that! I am proud of myself for that!

Most importantly, I hope that anyone who reads that feels more love for themselves and what they dream to feel! Loving yourself is such an important part of life and opens all of us up to loving and being loved by others.

Feeling versus thinking has been a big theme in my life's stack of "lessons for Justin to learn". I love to think, to process, to organize, to strategize and plan and those are great skills. I can certainly get wrapped up in my head thinking about something. However, I am a deep, sensitive soul and when I get out of my own way, I can feel through any decision. My gut will never lead me in the wrong direction and this connectedness is a gift that all of us have. That is part of the magic! For me it is about learning to use my thinking brain when I need it...and then put it aside and simply be open and feel! If there is one thing to take away from this blog post, I hope you are able to connect with the idea of living with a desire for a feeling vs. living with a desire for status or achievement. Opening ourselves to what feels great, which is something that is available to all of us, right now.

Throughout our lives, we are all presented with opportunities for self-reflection and growth. Sometimes they're opportunities that are subtle and sometimes they are like a big truck hitting us that knocks us down. Whether they are subtle nudges from the universe like a comment a friend makes, or maybe a message that appears in our world a few times, (you know like when your friend says something in passing, you see that scenario play out in a show, movie or book, and then you see it written on a billboard on your way home) opportunities for self-reflection and growth are everywhere and it is up to us to experience them. I often talk about how the universe will agitate us when we are not on the right path, or perhaps when it is time to change course in some area of our life. I think I missed a lot of these subtle messages. Seriously, I KNOW I missed a lot of these...and that's totally ok. I see these nudges (or kicks in the pants) as a message to center, to be aware of what my soul is calling for and to really try to LISTEN (because we do know the answer if we listen). In my life it ended up being a cancer diagnosis that pushed me to really start the healing process. It was this big, public experience that shifted my life and gave birth to my "new normal" and this amazing, new life that I am living. With that said, it doesn't take a brain tumor to have a fresh start in your life or to give birth to your own new normal. When you set intentions for your life and follow those with consistent action in the direction of your best self, everything is possible. I am grateful for this.

The video below was recorded the night before I wrote the blog post above and I included it so that you can really see that the way I was communicating publicly on the blog, and privately with myself, were in sync. In the video I acknowledge that "I am a little nervous" and then verbally affirm that I have "been envisioning myself waking up tomorrow feeling good" followed by my main positive mantra while I take the dose of chemo. This is a great example of honoring what you are experiencing and also using your positive thoughts, words and visualizations to improve your experience-in this case honoring that I was nervous and affirming that I would get restful sleep and wake up feeling good.

Consistency is very important and when you form habits around this type of positive thinking and speaking you will notice a shift in every area of your life.

www.justinlevenson.com/strongerthanyouthink

CHAPTER 14
BLOG #13 | 7.16.14
Back to Work Baby!

Chapter affirmation: **My daily routine nurtures me and supports my healing. I love myself enough to make time for what supports my growth. I welcome self-loving habits into my life.**

Today was another big day in the life...I went back to work today for the first time in 5 months...seriously!!! It felt great to get active and return to the office. I am very thankful that I had the opportunity to take time to rest and heal after surgery and during treatment, but I was ready to do something, and it felt good to work today! Since my last post, I took the first of 12 chemo treatments which wasn't a huge ball of fun...but also not the worst thing in the world! I took the chemo 5 nights in a row, right before I went to bed in addition to twice daily Zophran, which is an anti-nausea medicine. The Zophran hasn't quite gotten rid of anything but it does help some. In general, I have had a pit in my stomach for the past 3 weeks and as I sit here, I haven't taken chemo for 16 days, I still feel "meh" in my stomach from the chemo. BUT...it's also not the worst thing in the world and I'm lucky to have the "good" kind of chemo that doesn't have the worst of the worst side effects. SO... I'll be glad when we push through all of the treatments and am very thankful that I am alive to have access to this medicine...but damn, I'll be glad to be done (I should be done by May 2015)!!

Alright...I pulled another half post b/c today is now Wednesday, 7/16/14 and I wrote the portion above yesterday, 7/15/14. What can I say, I was focused on blogging, started to blog and my Facebook messenger kept "dinging"...so I chatted with friends...then friends came over...and you see how I never got back around to the blog! :)

So today was day 2 back at work and it was good. My boss Bill was in today and so we had a good opportunity to chat about things (we both had lists for each other haha), get a game plan on a few immediate projects and talk about a few bigger picture thoughts! We work really well together, and it did my mind good to think again and I think especially so with someone as smart as Bill who I have known for a long time. Don't get me wrong, I have done a whole bunch of thinking over the past 5 months but it's a different vibe for me to be thinking about work again and it was feeling good. My mind is definitely ready to rock and now I'm just going to work on the body part as I navigate the remaining 11 more treatments! Get ready, b/c if you keep reading this blog, I'm sure you are going to get some count down action as I tackle the treatments! Whoop Whoop...11 more! hahaha!!

Over the past several months, one surprise gift was having the opportunity to spend time with so many of the amazing people that fill my life...in many cases it was just a normal hang with friends I see often, in some cases it was with friends that I never seemed to see often enough, and I have also met a ton of great people going through all of this! Thanks to having a brain tumor, I got to strengthen so many relationships in my life...sounds kinda funny to say that, and I am seriously laughing out loud when I say that but it's true...thanks to this experience I got to reach out and touch my network of people in a big way. Thankfully I believe we have all grown in some way through this and it's been awesome to experience this with all of you...here's to continuing that awesomeness! On one Thursday morning in June, I sat down with my friend Tim at Crema to catch up on life, which is thankfully going really well for both of us, so the vibe was awesome! At one point the conversation moved to the things we always want to get done for ourselves and many times throughout our lives, we did not get done...b/c we didn't make time for them. I told him about my attempts to do things for myself daily and that I had probably only been doing these things 2-3 days per week. These were my things I wasn't making time for...and I had a ton of time to make for it while being on medical leave...that was impactful for me. Tim told me about his daily checklist that he physically has on his wall. Tim wakes up every morning and physically checks off his daily list b/c he takes time for himself every day...that's awesome! I left our hang so completely inspired to steal this idea (shamelessly of course) and made my own list of daily goals. I call it "Justin's Daily Kickstart" and my list is: Meditate, Exercise, take a mindful and thankful moment, think about and feel my goals, eat a healthy breakfast, read at least 5 pages, journal entry (blog, journal, video journal), write 1 "thank you" note! I have been waking up early enough to do this and it is awesome. I'm certainly not perfect with my 5 times per week but who cares...I'm close and it's feeling great! I thought this was important to share b/c 1. you may want to try something like that and 2. b/c it's another example of life giving you what you need and the fact that you never know where you will be inspired and where you can inspire others!

Thanks for reading and for all of your support!

Talk to you again soon!

Justin

Reflecting Back:

Well, in case you haven't heard or experienced it yourself, chemotherapy has a reputation for not always making you feel so great and this post clearly shows that...likely something you have experienced or know about. However, I love having examples like this where I can tell I was working to be honest, and also positive for myself. I was not feeling well after the first round of the stepped up, monthly double dose I would be on for 12 months and that is 100% ok. What I love is that I was having grateful, thankful thoughts and that I was able to shift my thoughts - if even for a few moments while I wrote the blog post - to thankful, grateful thoughts about friends, modern medicine, my boss Bill and the ability to think about work again. The daily kick start I mention was really helpful for me too. I love lists and I also love carving out time for myself in the morning for the things I know I need. Perhaps there is a morning routine waiting for you? Or something you want to prioritize for yourself every day? I'm a big fan of all of us doing what we know we need for ourselves and making that a priority! Loving ourselves enough to make "me time" a priority is really important. For me, my mornings are sacred and are the times that feel the best for me to create daily habits. You may prefer some time in the afternoon, or perhaps in the last hours before you go to sleep. Hell, you may want to spread out your love throughout the day, or maybe just live a life dedicated to what you know you crave and need.

Maybe you start with a 5-minute meditation once per day or perhaps a goal of having one grateful and thankful thought once per day. Or maybe it is a list of 10 things that take 3 hours...all of these are great and whatever works for you is the perfect place to start. My point is that when we listen to ourselves and are open to learning more, we will know what feels right and will be able to fill our experiences with the thoughts, actions and people that nurture us and support our growth. It doesn't matter what or who fits that description but rather that we set out with the intention to listening, prioritizing our own life and loving ourselves enough to make time for loving and supporting our own experience. Listening and loving deeply.

Are you ready to create your own morning kickstart or daily self-love routine? This can start with one thing and grow as large as you want it to. Seriously, if this seems like a lot to you, pick one thing that resonates with you and start there. Most importantly there is zero pressure to be perfect...zero pressure.

I am told it takes at least 21 days to form a habit so how about a 21-day kickstart challenge? Create your own kickstart list (and remember it can be a list of one) and make a commitment to yourself to do this for 21 days. I suggest that you start small with one or two things you want to include on your list. Some ideas to get you started are: exercise for 10 minutes, read one page of a book, sit quietly for 1 minute every morning to think about things you are grateful for, eat a healthy breakfast, etc. Think about the habits you currently have, habits you have thought about creating in your life, and perhaps some of the new tools you have learned in this book. Now text, call or email a few friends about your new commitment, because we all need accountability partners!

For an extra dose of positivity, inspiration and motivation, here is a video where I talk about my new morning routine and how great it feels.

www.justinlevenson.com/strongerthanyouthink

CHAPTER 15
BLOG 14 | 8.31.14
Keeping This Party Going...

Chapter affirmation: **I bring peace to my life and everyone in it. Through my daily life, I inspire others to be their best.**

Happy Sunday friends! It is an overcast day here in Nashville, perfect for Sunday chilling with the French press and Spotify playlists! Big news of the day...I didn't let myself procrastinate this blog post any longer...yup.... it's obviously been longer than I expected! Ooops! hahaha! I would like to tell you a story about this one big, exciting, romantic, thrilling, growth filled, up and down experience...but...thankfully, that's the way I would describe every day of my life over the past month and a half since my last post! Life continues to be absolutely AMAZING! (sorry for the all caps...hopefully I made my point) :)

Most importantly, my health continues to move in the right direction as my body responds perfectly to treatment, my lab results are great, I'm pretty sure my MRI from two weeks ago was great b/c I haven't heard anything from Vanderbilt, but my oncologist will confirm that on the 8th when I see him (I already know...but it IS nice to get confirmation from him) :) I just finished month 3 of 12 of the final round of chemo. In case you forgot, this consists of taking chemo pills at home before bed, 5 nights in a row per month and then taking 3 weeks off.... AND... repeat 12 times! So... round 2 was better than round 1 and round 3 was better than round 2! You like my trend here don't cha'? ME TOO! The monthly cycle is pretty predictable at this point and by today (almost one week out of treatment) I feel pretty good and that trend will continue daily until it's time for the next chemo dose...and repeat! It's the ebb and flow of treatment that is certainly in line with the ebb and flow of the universe... just as this whole experience has been! In the flow 100%!

Don't get me wrong, I still find myself getting a little anxious before treatment...I even video myself starting treatment each month to document these emotions...I think it is very interesting to observe this about myself and grow through it. In addition to a little anxiety when it's time to take chemo, the nausea isn't quite "fun" yet but it's manageable. I added the use of some essential oils which seem to have helped the Zophran in the fight to settle out my stomach! So... for any of my friends that may have been worried that my positive attitude and seemingly superhuman ability to not have a bad day while going through cancer treatment was a cover for buried emotions, etc. I promise I'm being real! :) Brain surgery and cancer treatments, no matter how successful, haven't been all roses...but who cares...I'm alive baby! :)

All of this said.... I can't stress how amazing I feel in general, how amazing life is and how this whole thing continues to be overwhelmingly positive, exciting and honestly fires me UP!!!

Last week was my 7th week back to work at SESAC full-time, and it's going really well! I love being active, using my brain, being around people and let's face it, being involved in successful projects is always exciting and we have plenty of those at SESAC right now! Thankfully, SESAC continues to be an amazing supporter of mine. I've said it many times in this blog, but it's worth repeating that the love of people around me, including my SESAC family has been such a key factor in my quick recovery and success in treatment! I am very thankful!

Throughout the past 7 months, I've been spending a lot of time journaling and documenting this journey in a more private way than this blog, and all of this may see some light of day, later down the road (or not which is great too). One of the great things about having this outlet to just let it all out.... speak my mind...write it down.... say it loud...etc....has been some "ah ha" moments that pop up! Sometimes I think "this could be a chapter in my book", "...or maybe a talking point in a lecture..."...who knows my friends! I do know that when I just opened my journal, the page that jumped out was about the idea of "Actionable Inspiration" from 8/10/14 (one of those "ah ha" moments I mentioned). Lately I've been thinking about "actionable inspiration", as it relates to ways to inspire people and do it in a way that leaves them feeling ready to take action, ready to take that step, forgive that friend or relative, face your chronic illness, or a long list of the things we all think about wanting to do more of, be better at, find peace with, etc. At this point in my life, for me, it's about sharing my story honestly to other people, not judging them for their step on their path and loving them more. But what about you? How can you inspire more people? How can you start?

The trick is that none of us have to have a brain tumor and brain cancer to be inspired and awakened and most importantly ready to inspire others...for me, this brain stuff just happened to be where my path leads me. How can we teach other people to see this, ultimately love more, let go and release more so that we mindfully plant and feed the seeds of peace, prosperity and healing? I will continue to share my story in an honest, open way b/c this not only helps inspire others, but it also helps me work through the deep emotions that have come with the past 7 months. So, what about you? What can you do right now to give you more peace about something? Who can you send a quiet "I love you" to? If nothing comes to mind, that's ok...just opening up to it is an amazing first start. You could try saying one of these in your head in the moments before drifting off to sleep, or first thing in the morning or when you say your daily prayers: "I bring peace to my life and everyone in it", "Through my daily life, I inspire other people to be their best", "I radiate love and peace" and while you are at it maybe this one "I have perfect health" b/c let's face it...we all want that! :)

If nothing else, please know that If You Can Think It, You Can Have It! :)

I really appreciate everyone's continued support and love.

Here's to a new week full of peace, love and lots of great times!

Justin

Reflecting Back:
Ah the continued ups and downs of our lives! This post is another example of some of my ups and downs and also of a few tools I use in my life every day and talk about when I have the opportunity. The first example I see is that I continue to keep my mantra at the front of my mind and thus in my words. There is an excerpt from it here with "...as my body responds perfectly...". This is so important! By now, you know that when we develop and use positive mantras and affirmations, we send consistent, positive and impactful messages to our subconscious mind. This consistency is where the magic happens and when we share these mantras with our tribe, it amplifies the positivity. And who doesn't want that?

The more that we keep our focus on positive outcomes (aka. our dreams, affirmations and mantras) the better, but what happens when we notice that our thoughts, words, and/or actions have reverted back to a not so positive place? An easy answer is that we can express thanks for the self-awareness to notice this! And once we express that gratitude, and are aware, all it takes is for us to lovingly bring our focus back to the positive (to our center), to the grateful moments in our life and our positive affirmations and mantras. I really try to own the low moments as much as I own and celebrate the high moments and I am always thankful for the self-awareness to know when I need to change course or as some would say "check your self, before you wreck yourself." After all, I am human and a total work in progress too and by loving the self-awareness, we are continuing to strengthen and build faith in the process. Trust the process!

This post also brings to light a few other tools that I was learning and practicing then, that I still work to keep in my life today. Tools like essential oils, creative writing/self-expression, and certainly the continued use of positive affirmations, and meditative mantras. All of these tools have helped me cultivate a home base, my center, a positive attitude to come home to when I show my inevitable human self and notice my mind in worry, frustration, loneliness, etc.

As your healing journey continues, remember to always love yourself by surrounding and comforting your body with an environment for healing. Essential oils are a natural tool that can be really impactful for this aspect of your journey. I used them during and after my cancer treatment and I still use many today too. There are several brands on the market that offer a variety of oils and oil blends and you can find them at most grocery and health food stores as well as numerous online retailers.

Essential oils helped me create an environment for healing in my body with calming effects from plants like lavender, liver support from lemon essential oil and a great oil blend, DigestZen from an essential oil company doTerra. DigestZen applied topically on my digestive area made a noticeable difference in my side effects from chemotherapy. In simple terms, when I started using this product, my nausea decreased, and it is worth a try.

Thankful   8/ 9/22/14

Very thankful right now.
Happy, watching the sun set
    over this great city

Thankful for the lessons
the loving, the learning
and the letting go
I love the feeling I get
when I reflect on what
has happened, what this,
what this can + will be!

It's all very exciting, So
Damn exciting. But,
Most of all, most importantly
   I am Thankful!

CHAPTER 16
BLOG 15 | 10.2.14
Ups and Downs...Life is Good!

Chapter affirmation: **I honor every step in my journey and am grateful for the awareness. I am grateful. I am supported through every experience in my life. I grow through my experiences.**

So, it's Thursday afternoon, I was about to procrastinate this blog post again and won't let that happen again today!

I'm feeling great today! I finished the fourth round of chemo 12 days ago and per the normal, monthly cycle, I am feeling MUCH better. 4 down, 8 to go...I've got this! My last MRI and labs were great and I'm on track to start month 5 in two weeks. So... short story is, it's all working, and my body is responding perfectly to treatment!

The chemo continues to be...well...chemo! What I mean is that it continues to make me feel fatigued, lose my appetite, feel some nausea and just overall feel "meh" (meh=a technical/medical word of course) :) It is very much a cycle and the side effects seem to peak around day 8 of the monthly treatment cycle. It's manageable and like I've said many times.... beats being dead! :) no really! haha!

The simple status...I'm doing really well, enjoying the journey and honoring the highs and lows!

The past few weeks have been a little more emotional for some reason! I mean, look...I know in general what the reasons are, but it hasn't been just one thing on my mind; more so just a heaviness. After 8 months of the ups and downs mentally and physically, the idea of a marathon came to my mind and I am right in the middle of it with 8 months of treatment to go!

My faith in an amazing end result has never been stronger but emotionally and physically I found myself needing to dig a little deeper than normal and really work to keep my mind focused. It's all a process, and I honor that...some days lately have just been a little tougher than others!

The good news...there is always good news...I'm glad I can be honest with myself and work through it! I'm thankful for my family and friends who help me talk through all of this and listen with open hearts...they make those days much easier! Hell, it comes and goes and most of the time life is absolutely awesome and I forget that I even have cancer. What does cancer feel like anyway? My cancer doesn't hurt me, sometimes it scares me, but it doesn't hurt me! Drugs are the gifts that make you pay for their joy...I think it's a worthy trade of course, but you know you are taking them, and nothing is free! So yeah, the drugs are a short-term pain, for a long-term gain and I'm cool with that!

I've been talking to a lot of my friends about natural ways to promote perfect health and also help my body fight cancer! I LOVE this! Ultimately, we are what we eat and eating well is key. In addition to eating well, there are so many things we can be doing and that I will share as I get more into them. My rule has been that I run everything by my oncologist and he loves questions! After taking a list of great ideas to him recently, his feelings were that he knows that the chemo I am taking is very effective against the type of cancer I have; it is the current best practice! What he doesn't know is how effective it is in combination with several other things (the natural health ideas/supplements/etc.). His suggestion is that for the next 8 months, I keep it to my warm lemon water daily, essential oils and also a whey protein supplement that was suggested b/c this boosts my glutathione. The glutathione has something to do with my immune system and there are actually clinical trials going on at Vanderbilt exploring this idea but currently only on the more serious brain tumors. PS: I'm ok with the type of brain tumor I had vs. being eligible for that trial and wish them well!

All of this said, after I am done with chemo I can throw every healthy idea against the wall, eat really well and be healthier than ever before! Score! It's all a balance and this is true for my treatment and defeat of cancer too!

I hope life is continuing to be great for all of you...thanks for reading!

Justin

Reflecting Back:
Ah the highs and lows of life...we all experience them. Sometimes I think they may sneak by us as we move so quickly in our routines and sometimes, they are so extreme that we can't even think about our routines and we are forced to experience them fully, in that moment. For everyone I have met, a cancer diagnosis has likely been more on the extreme side of things and it certainly was for me. However, throughout this larger, extreme experience, I found so many smaller ups and downs, so many opportunities to be in the moment and to experience that moment as fully as possible-certainly more than I ever had up until that point. Whether it was the ebb and flow of chemo effects throughout the day, or starting the day of radiation therapy feeling great, only to be completely whipped out by the end of the day; highs and lows were a constant throughout my cancer journey...but aren't they always a constant to some degree?

If you are anything like me, you can wake up healthy, feeling great, loving life and then bam...a phone call with bad news, a frustrating exchange with family or a friend, or how about a customer service call with a telecom company (those are a blast right?). When we are present in our lives, or at least trying to be present, we are able to notice and experience these moments and when needed, bring ourselves back to our center...the place we are working to cultivate and grow. The place we all have access to, that feels safe, feels positive, and feels like home... because it is home, on the journey to our best self.

In the post above, I love that I am being honest and kind with myself at this stage in the journey. This post speaks my truth at the time and shows that yeah, I was not feeling 100% all the time and sometimes I would even say that I felt pretty rough. And yet at the same time, it shows that despite anything I may have been experiencing at some point in my day, I was able to find things to be grateful for and moments to laugh, smile, have fun and find what some may call "the silver lining". It's all about balance and love.

Honoring where we are, despite how much we may want to be elsewhere, is powerful! This can mean that you notice yourself in a less than positive pattern, or perhaps one starting to creep back in your lives. You can be honest with yourself about the great times, sure that is easy. But, how about when things don't go the way you had hoped...those times when you screwed up or perhaps disappointed yourself or someone you love? Those are the times that I think you should be extra aware of where you are, truly honor that place as you celebrate your self-awareness and then lovingly bring yourself back to your center, on the way to your best self. I know that this is something that I still focus on today and I hope that when you find yourself in a similar place, you are able to honor the moment, love yourself fully and lovingly come home to your center...the place where you feel safe, comforted and supported...on your way to your best self!

Here is a video from October of 2014 that is a great example of the ups and downs of my cancer journey as well as my attempts to honor all of them. You will notice that as I become aware of my emotions and work to process them, I use my mantra, sense of humor, and positive nature to re-center myself.

www.justinlevenson.com/strongerthanyouthink

Here's who I am
      or better yet who I thought I was...
I want you all to know that this is a positive
story with a whole lot of great times
and an ending that while not always
      a very positive story...I promise.
There are a few keywords I want you to pay
attention for... LOVE! Anxiety!
Brain Tumor! Cancer!? Positivity! More LOVE!
B/C you see this positive story, with these
important themes that I am talking about
is my life... it is me...and it has is the about
most exciting, transformational experience
I have ever witnessed. -also intro 2 steps positive
                                              creativity +
                                              affirmations.

It's easy to say this started on 2/3/14 when
I had a seizure at work, woke up surrounded
by paramedics to later find out I had a
brain tumor but NO, that's not when
this started... AT ALL!
You see there's just the continuation of the
divinely guided path I have been on
my entire life! Holly likely longer than
these bones have been around!

CHAPTER 17
BLOG #16 | 2.1.15
What a Year!!

Chapter affirmation: **I grow closer to my highest potential every day. I grow towards my best self every day.**

Hello friends!

First, we should catch up...Happy Thanksgiving, Happy Holidays and Happy New Year! I know it has been WAY too long since my last post and for all of you that have been asking me, my family and my friends how I have been doing...the answer is that life is beautiful!

Now, by me telling you "life is beautiful" doesn't mean the past couple of months have been a breeze, pain-free, totally easy or any other phrase that makes you think it was all "rainbows and sunshine!" BUT... every single day that I wake up, I feel thankful to be alive, thankful to be surrounded by so much love and flat out LUCKY! No matter how much stress I may feel or how rough the chemo makes me feel, I can always find an opportunity to be thankful, to step back, take a breath (or several) and find a thankful place in my heart! This is huge for me b/c at times, these small moments of stress, tension, possibly feeling overwhelmed, etc. seem MUCH bigger than they really are and being able to take a step back has been a big thing for me. Sometimes it takes a real conversation with my family or friends and sometimes it just takes getting some rest (sometimes I can be a butt when I'm tired and don't feel well..."keeping it 100")! Regardless of what it takes or what causes these moments of tension, it's a beautiful gift to be able to take these steps back. I truly believe that this isn't a cancer thing and that we all have these moments in our lives where we need to take a step back, count to 10, take a few deep breathes, etc....here's to finding what helps you keep it all in perspective and find peace in these moments!

Most importantly, my health is continuing to improve! All of my MRI's have been looking good, my labs have been completely normal, and I am about to start month 9 of 12 of my chemo regimen. I can see the light at the end of tunnel and it feels so damn good! The good thing is that the monthly chemo dose is consistent...and the bad thing is that it is consistent. What I mean is that so far, the monthly side effects from chemo have not gotten worse which is the good news. The bad thing is that it still makes me feel like I am getting the flu every month. I thought of a good response to the question I always get "How is chemo going?" and my response is "It is going really well inside my body, which means that I don't always feel well!" I know in my heart that my body is responding perfectly to treatment and that I will live a really long life. This gut feeling makes the 10 days per month that I don't feel well completely worth it! I often say, "this is a short-term pain for a long-term gain!"

When I turned 36 in December, I landed on two wishes for my new year and those are great health and love and my #1 goal this year is to find amazing ways to leverage my experiences to help other people! From the moment I knew I had a brain tumor, I knew this was going to be about growth. I immediately knew it was about helping other people and later learned that the first and most important step was going to be helping myself! My life is certainly not "fully helped" (to use my own weird analogy) but that's ok...wouldn't it be boring to be perfect today? I mean, really...what would we have to work on for the rest of our lives?

I always knew that this whole cancer thing was going to create more opportunities to help other people and until recently I was holding back planning my steps as my focus was solely on healing first and documenting the journey second. As the calendar turned to 2015,

I opened up my realm to my #1 goal and began to start putting my mind on it! Regardless of whether or not I end up being a best-selling author, top-rated speaker, entertainment executive or move home to Birmingham to work in the furniture business with my dad (sorry dad, this isn't something I am considering but just used as an example haha) I know that what brings me the most joy in my heart is helping other people be more awesome than they think they can be. To take this a step further, it makes me feel indescribable joy to show people how the power of positivity can completely transform our lives. We have to know that this can prepare us to handle life's speed bumps in a healthy way and when life happens, and we are unprepared, that there are tools that can help us navigate these bumps in a healthy way (regardless of how we are conditioned when life happens). I have mentioned several of these ideas and tool sets throughout the past year and look forward to exploring this realm more as I learn more and pass this on to all of you! Whether this is over coffee, lunch, a book, on a stage or sitting in my living room; I love these types of conversation and can't wait to keep on chewing on these types of universal topics with you all!

As the 1-year anniversary of my seizure approaches (2/3/15), I find myself having another opportunity to reflect (insert my mind immediately saying, "haven't you reflected enough?" haha). The first thing I want to say again is THANK YOU! No really, THANK YOU! No matter who you are, how many times we have spoken or hung out during the past year or hell, whether we have even met in "real life" or not...you have helped me, and I wouldn't be here without you! The support that you have all shown me continues to blow me away and helped make the past 12 months so much easier! My first "I love you" goes to my family b/c they have been my rock and, on those days, when I was feeling low (like last Wednesday after work), they are always there to Skype or talk and let me know they love me and that everything will be ok! Next you know I have to thank Jill, my boss's assistant who walked by my office at the exact moment I had the seizure and is responsible for me being at Vanderbilt within an hour of a big seizure...and I believe being alive today! My friends have been so amazing, and I won't begin to name them b/c you wouldn't want to read such a long list of amazing people (and I would certainly forget a ton of people) ...but you know who you are, and I appreciate you! The one household I do want to think is the Handley household who so graciously hosted me for three weeks after surgery (b/c I couldn't be alone), made sure I took my meds at the right time (seriously had to take so many meds) and were there to support me when I found out I had brain cancer in what I call the "kick in the nuts appointment" with my oncologist after surgery (to review the pathology report). I would be remiss without thanking the Handley's dogs too b/c wow...I needed that love too and they knew I needed their furry dog-love. My doctors know how thankful I am and Vanderbilt in general knows that they have a supporter, fundraiser and champion for life...this hospital and everyone there are amazing and the level of care I have received is second to none! I also want to send a general thank you to the Music Row community that wrapped their arms around me in so many ways. From an "Uber Fund" to help while I couldn't drive, to t-shirts on the Round-a-Bout statues to the countless messages, emails, visits, etc... this community made me feel so amazingly loved...thank you! One day while talking about opportunities that were presented to me outside of Nashville, Mr. Bob Oermann stressed that I can't leave Nashville and that no matter what, when I needed it, that this community would be there for me! I think we were really talking about professional opportunities, but WOW was he right...this community has taken care of me and I am forever grateful! Thanks Bob!

There are several amazing organizations that have stepped up to help me this year and I can't wait to be able to help them help more people in the future. MusiCares and Meals2Heal are two organizations that you can support right now...or wait until I ask you myself. I also want to think "the best class ever" from Leadership Music (you rock)!

Check them out here:
www.grammy.org/musicares

www.heimerdingerfoundation.com
www.leadershipmusic.org

So, friends, it's been one hell of a year and I can't wait to see what the next year brings for all of us! I'm not exactly sure where my path will lead me, but I know that I will always have a home in Nashville and can't wait to continue walking this path with you all! Even on this gloomy Nashville Sunday, I can tell you that the future is bright friends!

Thank you for helping open my heart and for helping me learn to feel and give love like never before!

Justin

PS: I told you that I have been doing video journals throughout the past year! I have about 60 so far and I like to film all sorts of different moments. As a taste of the types of videos I have and as a reminder, here is where my mind is every time I go to sleep, wake up, take chemo and think about my life. Grateful, intentional and positive.

www.justinlevenson.com/strongerthanyouthink

Reflecting Back:
There is something special about anniversaries to me and this one-year mark was a big one...hell I am currently approaching the seven-year mark and I can't wait to celebrate! The idea of "stepping back" that I was talking about is an area of my life that I am continuing to grow in and one that I love. For me it is having self-awareness to know when I am either about to do or say something that I may later regret, or that I know is not my best self speaking. Sometimes it is noticing the thought

or pattern beginning and then being able to almost press pause, take a few breathes, or push save on that email draft so that you can make sure you are serving yourself, and others in the best possible way. The path of peace and love.

In these moments back in 2014, it was frustrations about my life's path, on top of stuff I was holding towards my family over the years, loneliness and the longing for love combined with not feeling very well without consistent great sleep. Sometimes it took (and still takes) the words and nudges from people close to me. At times I perceive signs in nature and in my everyday life as communication and reminders about myself, and how to live in the direction of my highest potential. And I am human...which means that many times I experience this growth through reflecting BACK on moments I wish I had handled differently. Things I wish I hadn't said, or a tone I wish I didn't use...an email I wish I would have changed...a phone call I wish I would have done differently...a frustrated comment to my girlfriend's sweet cat when she claws on the furniture... all moments where I was not living to my highest potential. **However, I am so grateful for the moments of reflecting back because this is school...this is growth in a very impactful way.** If we pay attention and remain open and honest with ourselves, I believe the lessons are worth far more than any momentary stress in our lives.

My passion for wellness on all levels, mind, body and spirit, has continued with full force. The "tools" I spoke of then are more in my life than ever before and I have been learning more about new ways to nurture our body and minds. Things like Ayurveda, natural supplements, Shamanism, targeted focused mediation to aide in the release of toxic emotions in our bodies and an overall release of negative, toxic emotions from my life. This area of thought and study feels so good to me, I know I will continue to learn and seek more and look forward to sharing this with our community. My life has been completely transformed since my cancer journey began and I am so thankful for the teachers that have come into my life through their writings, seminars, and friendly cups of coffee down the street. Inspiration and growth are everywhere, all around us, and all we have to do is be present, be open and enjoy!

This post is also another great example of my continued use of positive affirmations and mantras and sharing those with the people close to my life, which you now know magnifies the impact. The video I shared above, is one of many I recorded of me, working to own my moment, keep my dreams and affirmations front and center in my mind, while continuing to engage my friends and family. This affirmation of "my body responding perfectly to treatment..." and me "...emerging healthier, happier and more empowered to do great things" is so powerful because I deeply believe that this is concrete evidence of how the subconscious mind compels us to take action that supports the manifestation of our dreams. Me writing this book is 100% part of the manifestation of the work I was doing before and after this period of my life.

I am still so very thankful for the support that flowed to during the time I needed it the most-when I was going through the bulk of my treatments. I am also constantly filled with gratitude for the support that still fills my life today as I work to build a career helping, teaching and inspiring as many people in our world as I can. Knowing that every day I wake up, my purpose is to be in service to other people, is me living the life of my dreams and for that I am truly grateful. However, despite the continuous support and my heart overflowing with gratitude, there are still days that I feel nervous, uneasy, and scared. I own these days the best that I can, and it seems that just when a little nervous questioning comes into my mind, someone reaches out to express their gratitude for what I am doing and sharing with the world.

Whoa! This is such a powerful experience and I hope that when you are feeling something less than at peace and confident, your support system is there for you. We all need support in one way or another and I want you to know that you are never alone...never.

This desire to help you, is why I am writing this book and is why I ultimately left the comforts of my past career to set a course for this...for a life spent in service to others, to help as many people as I can, improve their experience now, and learn how to spark lasting change in their body, mind and spirit.

The universe will always be in perfect time and will give us all of the opportunities to prepare for our moments. My hope is that I can continue to grow towards my highest potential and share what I learn on the way with anyone that may want to learn with me. Thankful!

Can you think of a recent experience where you could have benefited from a few calming breathes to "step back" from a stressful situation? Maybe you can relate to sending a heated email that could have been softened or having a tense conversation with a family member or colleague, maybe even a doctor visit that didn't go as you had hoped? Chances are, you can relate, and when you experience moments like this in the future, try taking a few minutes to take slow, calming breathes and approach those experiences from a more centered place.

A great way to use your breath to calm down is to take a full, deep breath through your nose for 4 counts. Hold the breath for 4 counts at the top of your breath and then exhale fully through your mouth. For your second breath, change the exhale to a slow 4 count exhale through your nose. Repeat this slow exhale a few times and you will notice a calming shift that will help you approach life from a more calm, centered and peaceful place.

CHAPTER 18
BLOG #17 | 4.7.15
Do You Have a Favorite Number?

Chapter affirmation: **I feel joyful, peaceful and loving. My life feels like my dreams. I am at peace and on track.**

I'm not sure what my favorite number is...sometimes I think I default to 7, other times I love 9, over the past year I have been all about 3...but today is different! Today is different b/c today my favorite number is 11! I'm sure I can think of several meaningful "11's" in my life right now but the most important 11 that is on my mind right now is that...last night I started chemo cycle #11 which means the last cycle (#12) is right around the corner! Can I get a HELL YES from the interwebs!!!!

Last week's labs cleared me to start cycle 11 and in the words of so many friends and actors "It's on!"...I'm so damn excited! During the past 14 months there have been a few key milestones that I have used as focus points for my journey. The short term was being able to go home after surgery, then starting the chemo/radiation therapy (that was a big ole bag of nerves), of course the next was my last radiation therapy. When I started the 1st of 12 monthly chemo cycles I remember saying "1 down, 11 to go" and celebrating that the sooner I started the sooner I would finish. I even remember thinking that "...wow, it will be great to be at cycle #11 and be able to see the finish line!"

Well friends...I can see the finish line and now have only 9 more nights of chemo therapy over the next 5 weeks...I'm close!

There has also been one "long term" vision, which is Labor Day 2015! Labor Day 2015 has always been the vision in my mind of being at least 3 months out of all chemo drugs and feeling great, feeling the most like Justin and most importantly a new, improved, healthier, happier, more peaceful Justin! Thanks to Vanderbilt this new improved version of myself can still walk, talk, laugh and enjoy the hell out of life...albeit with the bonus that I remember more of it b/c it is all happening without my friends bourbon and red wine! haha...WHO CARES...I'm alive and feeling great and don't miss it at all!

I made myself sit down and write this morning after I did a video journal last night. This is a big week for me...seriously...a big week! There isn't anything monumental happening that I know about other than being in a great headspace, feeling great, waking up after the first night of chemo, doing a little exercise and about to head out to my favorite little coffee shop in town, Edgehill café. (It's the people that make it great for me). All of that said, feel free to invite me to dinner or introduce me to your amazing, single girlfriend or hell, I will even except random gift cards! :) Seriously, just send some positive and peaceful energy my way, celebrate with me and do something nice for a friend today...that will be awesome!

This week is big because in the marathon of cancer treatment and life I have been on for 14 months, at times I have felt worn down emotionally and physically. Seriously...sometimes balancing the pressure of treatment, life, work, friends, family, etc. has been a lot to handle. Through all of my lower moments, I am thankful to find inspiration in the feeling that we all falter and have down moments, we all need to improve and continue on our own journey towards peace, happiness, prosperity and more peace! This human failure that I see in myself inspires me greatly! I have been conditioned to be a positive thinker my whole life and throughout this journey have found that no matter how conditioned I am, at times I let my mind get the best of me and succumb to the anxiety and emotions of the moment! That's ok...it really is.... we have to keep working at this, we have to keep centering ourselves and know that we are capable of manifesting the life we want to live!

We are all beautifully, imperfect humans and let's celebrate that...even if it's momentarily right now.... say thank you in your mind! :)

I hope we all have great weeks that take us closer to our goals!

Have an awesome day!

Justin

Reflecting Back:

Wow, what an amazing place to be after 14 months of cancer surgery and treatment. This blog post shows how I continued to create and use powerful, positive visions for the future in combination with the positive affirmations and visualizations I had created and been using to improve my experience immediately. The image of being at the 11th monthly chemo round and seeing the finish line combined with the Labor Day image I had of myself, feeling great, being active and having fun, are so powerful for me. Even something as simple as envisioning ourselves waking up feeling good, feeling rested and happy are powerful messages to send to our minds. These techniques have really helped me, and I know they will help you too.

By now, you also know that the really powerful impact comes when you combine feeling the emotions of your win with your positive affirmations and visualizations. **Simply put, feeling how the realization of your dreams feel. Feeling the emotions of your win.**

As I hope you can tell by this point, consistency is a big part of what makes all of this powerful. From creating more peace to manifesting perfect health, the commitment to thinking and speaking in a positive way and returning there when we find that we have drifted elsewhere, is the "magic" combination, and this power exists within you right now.

Here is a video from the night before this post that really highlights my continued, conversational use of my mantra and some of my early conceptual thoughts about this book, a true manifestation of my dreams.

www.justinlevenson.com/strongerthanyouthink

EPILOGUE
So, what happened next...

Well friends, the blog above was the last post on my blog and from there forward, until recently, I used Facebook as the primary way to communicate. I suppose I kept waiting for a moment when I would release my thoughts in a more formal way...a moment when I was "ready" and "prepared", and I suppose that I am there now because I am writing this book and loving life so much.

My last chemo treatment was actually the best of all of them because of the endorphins and emotional highs I was on...I AM ALMOST DONE is a likely good theme for that last week of chemo. It was the party at the end of a long road together...adios Chemo...adios! Here is a video from that awesome moment in May of 2015.

 www.justinlevenson.com/strongerthanyouthink

Life was instantly back to a new normal. After a year and a half of a medical schedule with at least a monthly follow up scheduled with my doctor (now six months) and life was...getting back to normal. Almost so much that over time I believe I started to get complacent in my lack of satisfaction with where my life was. I was lazy and afraid to do anything about it.... all from someone who is a very type A, motivated person.

For some reason, it was not quite time to make a professional and personal change in many areas. Professionally I always knew that the amazing family I worked with at SESAC would eventually become the amazing family I used to work with. I knew that my true passion to help, teach and inspire people versus what I used to think were my music industry aspirations would eventually propel me on to new challenges, but I never made a jump...I never owned it and went for it...until I did.

Thankfully in early 2016 I had another one of those real talk conversations with my dad who highlighted the past two years, my current position in my life and frustration with my professional direction.

That day, I decided I was going to leave my amazing job and amazing company I worked with to take a new direction in my life. I didn't know exactly what I was going to do, but I knew I wanted to do something different and there was no reason not to do that now. I had forgotten on some level that I had survived a near death experience and was reminded to seize this opportunity because we never know when our official last day in this life will be. Fear was holding me back and fear is what I knew I had to face. My dad always taught me to know F.E.A.R. as an acronym for False Evidence Appearing Real but it is always easier to coach someone else through that process than understanding it for myself and it was now time to face my fear and go for it.

My time at SESAC was amazing and they could have charged people for the real-world business and leadership skills I learned from my colleagues. I often lovingly refer to my time there as being paid to go to school because I learned and grew so much. With that said, the people that I worked with are like family and they loved and supported me through this period in my life when I needed their love and support the most. I am forever grateful for the fifteen plus years we shared together. Lately, I have been reflecting on the idea that the universe will continue to send us agitations in our lives when we are not doing what we are supposed to be doing...or perhaps we may have missed the point...

missed the lesson we needed to learn before we move to the next phase in our lives. In my life it can be frustrations, stress I bring on, tension, etc. and these are not good for me nor do they serve my higher purpose. But, they are definitely guideposts and loving nudges to help us along the path, in the direction of our highest, best self. Hell, sometimes these "nudges" feel more like big kicks in the pants. You know, like the day you found out you or a loved one has Cancer or a terminal condition.

Perhaps the trick for all of us is to view these subtle or not so subtle nudges as opportunities to grow closer to our best selves? Opportunities to take a little deeper look in the mirror, to center and listen, and to use that awesome self-awareness that we are working to cultivate, to find a gift in a place where we may not have expected to find one. Ultimately, seizing the opportunity to love ourselves as much as we can in that moment and be grateful for it.

I am more than seven years out of the first seizure, totally healthy and even healthier than I have ever been, in love with an amazing soul that I knew immediately was supposed to be in my world. I am setting out to live the life of my dreams...a life of service to others through teaching and sharing ideas that have helped me and that I am passionate about.

My immediate hope for you is that you have learned at least one thing in this book that helps you today, right now in the moment you are experiencing now. Whether that is a breathing exercise, new exercise or diet ideas, learning how to be intentional with your thoughts, tools to manage anxiety, or your own combination of everything I mentioned in this book; I am sharing this to help you right now!

Beyond offering ways to help you in this moment, I also hope that something in this book will inspire you to form new habits that feel good to you. New habits that have the power to transform your life in the most positive way you can imagine. We are all beautiful works in progress and through my own journey, I have found what fills my heart with maximum love and joy and am working to share that with the world. The goal is to help people be more awesome than they think they can be, and help people live a more balanced, peaceful and fulfilled life. Helping people transform their lives as I continue to transform my own.

My current life is the life of my dreams and I work intensely with loving gratitude to ensure my future feels even better than I can imagine my "painting" feels like today. I hope for that or better for all of us.

With love and gratitude!

Justin

P.S: If you are interested in learning more about the ideas I shared in this book, and how you can use them to create an environment for healing in your body, mind and spirit, please visit my website at www.justinlevenson.com and be sure to join the conversation on whichever social media platform you prefer. My goal is to help you form as many healthy habits as you want to create in your life, and I have several free resources available for you right now. Let's walk this path together, on the way to our best selves.

The End.
Not! It's just the beginning!

A SPECIAL INVITATION
Powerful Healing Affirmations

When you or someone you love receives a cancer diagnosis, activating the healing power of your mind is a very important part of your healing process. This is why I want you to have these powerful affirmations that I used during my cancer journey. These will help you heal your mind and body, reduce anxiety and ... get better sleep.

Visit JustinLevenson.com/strongerthanyouthink for these special gifts.

Please connect with me personally on Facebook, Instagram and Twitter @JustinLevenson, or at JustinLevenson.com

I look forward to connecting soon.

A POWERFUL BONUS
You Are Stronger Than You THINK Affirmations

Think it, See it, Feel it, Live it!

Ch2 : My surgery will be a perfect procedure.

Ch3 : I am grateful for today and for everyone who loves me.
I am open to love and to be loved.

Ch4 : With every breath, I release what no longer serves me.

Ch5 : I move in the direction of what is best for me. My self-love is abundant.

Ch6 : My body is healing perfectly. I'm positively manifesting my dreams.

Ch7 : I will grow through this and become healthier and happier than ever before.

Ch8 : I create a chorus of positivity within my tribe.

Ch9 : My breath calms me. I honor every moment of my life. My life's journey is divinely guided.

Ch10 : I welcome this radiation into my body, to fulfill the promise of eradicating cancer from my body and I am thankful for those who administer it.

Ch11 : My body is responding perfectly to treatment. Creating and repeating impactful thoughts and words helps me through my journey.

Ch12 : I welcome love into my life in every way. I am loved, supported and cared for.

Ch13 : Everything in my life has prepared me for everything in it. My life feels amazing and grows peacefully every day. I welcome love, peace and prosperity into my life.

Ch14 : My daily routine nurtures me and supports my healing. I love myself enough to make time for what supports my growth. I welcome self-loving habits into my life.

Ch15 : I bring peace to my life and everyone in it. Through my daily life, I inspire others to be their best.

Ch16 : I am grateful. I honor every step in my journey and am grateful for the awareness. I am supported through every experience in my life. I grow through my life experiences.

Ch17 : I grow towards my best self every day. I grow closer to my highest potential every day.

Ch18 : My life feels like my dreams. I feel joyful, peaceful and loving. I am at peace and on track.

ACKNOWLEDGEMENTS

This book was written over a seven-year period with a singular goal of impacting you and your loved ones, so that your life may be better because you read it. As with every successful project I have been involved with, a great team is vital, and this book is the sum of so many beautiful parts.

I am deeply indebted to Dr. Yanjun Ma, M.D. Ph.D. and Dr. Stephen W. Clark, M.D., Ph.D. for being a central part of my cancer journey. As a patient of these brilliant physicians, I was able to experience their loving and friendly bedside manner as well as benefit from their brilliant expertise and wisdom. I am flattered and grateful that they contributed their perspectives to this book.

I want to thank my editor Norbert Sieber, a wise man who I am grateful to know and call my friend. This book is better and more impactful to you because of his involvement and I am grateful that he shared his brain power and loving heart towards my mission of helping you spark lasting change in your body, mind and spirit.

I am thankful to Lauren Ledbetter for sharing her graphic design talent with the world and flexing her creative muscles for this book and my entire visual brand development. Lauren is a bright light in this world with a keen eye for design. Another keen eye for design that has made a huge impact on my life and this project is Luellyn Hensley. Not only did Luellyn introduce me to Lauren Ledbetter's amazing design work, Luellyn was the friend whose loving nudge convinced me to reach for my joy, write this book and create a life spent in service to others. Thank you Lu!

I am especially grateful to Judith Hill at Judith Hill Photography for not only capturing the most amazing pictures I have seen of myself but for her loving support through the process of conceptualizing, creating and publishing this book. Judith's passion for transformation and ability to see her client's true self made her the ideal photographer to be involved in this project.

My cancer journey may have started years before I was aware that there was a tumor growing in my body, but I will always see February 3, 2014 as the day it consciously began. This is the day that all of my loving colleagues at SESAC were there when I needed them the most. I am especially grateful for Jill Kemezis, Maxine Edwards, Cathy Grizzell and Bill Lee. I don't have a lot of firm memories about that day but from Jill walking past my office door at the exact moment that I began having a seizure, to Bill being by my side in the ambulance, to the constant love and support from Maxine and Cathy, my SESAC family was a huge part of my healing journey from the outset and I am deeply grateful for their love and support.

I have always heard that "team work makes the dream work" and this is certainly true in my life. My great friend Jon Romero has helped me from the beginning of this project. Jon set up the blog where I originally posted the blogs in this book and has been an instrumental resource; lovingly offering his wisdom and guidance on every aspect involved in this project. Thank you, Jon!

Throughout my life, and especially during my cancer journey I have been supported and lifted up by more amazing people than I can list here. I am eternally grateful for the love and support that my friends and family showed me during this journey and hope that they all know how much I appreciate them. Nashville, TN is a special place and I am lucky to be a part of this loving community.